D0312767
TL 233 B7 1978
3 0250 00429 8548

Tractor and Small Engine Maintenance

Fourth Edition

Tractor and Small Engine Maintenance

by

ARLEN D. BROWN

Associate Professor of Agricultural Mechanics
Agricultural Engineering Department
Purdue University

THE INTERSTATE
Printers & Publishers, Inc.

Danville, Illinois

REPRINTED WITH REVISIONS, 1978

Library of Congress Catalog Card No. 72-95181

Reorder No. 1546

PREFACE

This book has been written for tractor operators, ranchers, farmers, teachers and students, as well as for all who own or operate small engines of the kind which power lawnmowers, garden tillers and the like. Since the first three editions, entitled *Farm Tractor Maintenance,* dealt only with the subject of farm tractors, the title of the fourth edition has been changed to *Tractor and Small Engine Maintenance* in order to reflect this expanded coverage.

The need for preventive maintenance increases with the increase in tractor power, complexity and cost. Hopefully this book will assist the operator in preventing many costly unnecessary repairs.

Tractors and engines have been greatly changed and improved since the last revision. We have seen improvements in hydraulic systems, the increased use of hydraulically actuated power shift transmissions and the development of hydrostatic-type transmissions. Dry-type air cleaners have been adopted, and alternators have replaced generators on many models. Information on servicing and maintaining the new developments have been included in this edition.

Many new illustrations have been added.

The unceasing, untiring work of the late Ivan Gregg Morrison in the field of tractor maintenance has served as inspiration for the writing of this revision.

ARLEN D. BROWN

Note: In a continuing effort to keep the book up-to-date between major revisions, several picture substitutions have been made in the 1978 reprint. The General Reference List near the end of the book has been replaced with one citing some of the most recent and useful publications available.

ACKNOWLEDGMENTS

The author wishes to express gratitude and thanks to the following individuals and organizations for their advice, courtesy and generosity in making available many of the photographs and diagrams used throughout this book:

Allis-Chalmers Corporation, Milwaukee, Wisconsin
American Oil Company
J. I. Case Company
Dana Corporation, Toledo, Ohio
John Deere, Moline, Illinois
Detroit Diesel Engine Division, General Motors Corporation
Ethyl Corporation
Ford Tractor Operations, Ford Motor Co.
Hall-Toledo, Incorporated
C. N. Hinkle, Agricultural Engineer, American Oil Company
International Harvester Company
G. W. Isaacs, Agricultural Engineering, Purdue University
R. M. Lien, Agricultural Engineer, Purdue University
J. B. Liljedahl, Agricultural Engineer, Purdue University
Massey-Ferguson
The Oliver Corporation
Purdue University, Cooperative Extension Service
Clarence B. Richey, Agricultural Engineer, Purdue University
Snap-On Tools Corporation
Sun Electric Corporation
White Farm Equipment Co.

CONTENTS

PART I

INTRODUCTION

PART II

PREVENTIVE MAINTENANCE

PART III

OPERATION, REPAIR AND STORAGE

PART IV

SMALL ENGINES

Part I

INTRODUCTION

CHAPTER 1

MODERN FARM TRACTORS

The modern tractor is the result of many years of development. In fact, it wasn't until about 1876 that the steam traction engine was used extensively to pull large gangs of plows to turn the prairie sod.

In 1901 a large, clumsy gas traction engine weighing 20,000 pounds was rated at 22 horsepower at the drawbar and 45 horsepower on the belt. In 1911, near Lafayette, Indiana, 3 Oil-Pull traction engines were hitched to a 50 bottom plow for a demonstration. The big hitch plowed an acre every 75 seconds.

Here are some interesting dates in the development of tractors:

1850.........Portable steam engines pulled by horses for farm use
1876.........Steam traction engine used
1892–1901....Experimental models, gas traction engines
1903.........Gas traction engines produced commercially
1904.........Track-type traction engine
1906–07......The word "tractor" came into use
1908.........The first gasoline track-type tractor
1913.........Frameless or unit design in farm tractors
1915........."Motor cultivator" type tractor
1919.........Farm tractor equipped with power take-off
1920.........Starter and lights for tractors
1924.........Cultivating or tricycle-type tractor
1930.........Farm tractor equipped with power lift
1931.........First diesel-powered track-type tractor
1932.........Low-pressure rubber tires introduced for farm tractors

1935.........Factory-built, high-compression tractors to burn leaded gasoline
1935.........Hydraulic lift equipment on the tractor
1939.........Weight transfer for increased traction
1941.........First factory-built LP gas tractor
1944.........Power take-off and drawbar dimensions standardized
1946.........Transmission clutch for live power take-off
1949.........Hydraulic remote control cylinder dimensions standardized
1954–58......"On-the-go" and automatic shifting of tractor transmissions

Fig. 1-1—Three Rumley Oil-Pull kerosene burning tractors hitched to a 50 bottom plow in 1911.

TYPES

There are two general types of modern tractors, the wheel-type and track-type. The tractors in both groups range in size from the 1-2 plow to the 6, 8 or 10 plow. A recent development is the large, four-wheel drive tractor developing 160 to 180 PTO horsepower.

Courtesy John Deere, Moline, Ill.

Fig. 1-2—One of the new, large four-wheel drive articulated steering tractors with a turbocharged 531 cu. in. 6 cylinder diesel engine with a factory observed 175 PTO horsepower.

Wheel-type tractors are of three general kinds, the general-purpose row-crop, the utility and the four wheel standard. There are many variations of these, such as those used in an orchard or for high clearance, etc. General-purpose tractors are available with single front wheels, dual front wheels and adjustable front axle. Most of the tractors now have the adjustable front axle with tread spacing adjustable from about 50 inches to about 80 inches.

The rear wheel tread spacing with the regular axle is adjustable from about 65 inches to around 90 inches. Long axles are available making it possible to space the rear wheels to well over 100 inches.

Courtesy International Harvester Co.

Fig. 1-3—A large general-purpose tractor with a 550 cu. in. V-8 diesel engine with an estimated maximum 133 PTO horsepower.

Courtesy John Deere, Moline, Ill.

Fig. 1-4—A typical track-type tractor.

ENGINES

The External Combustion Engine

An external combustion engine is one in which the fuel is burned outside the cylinder and the power generated is confined in a separate container to be released through the cylinder. In the early steam traction engines, steam railroad locomotives and steam automobiles, fuel was burned to heat water and generate steam which was introduced into the cylinder through sliding valves. The steam was fed into the top of the cylinder for the down stroke and then into the bottom side of the piston for the return stroke giving a double acting piston for more efficiency and smoother action.

Courtesy John Deere, Moline, Ill.

Fig. 1-5—A standard diesel tractor.

Courtesy Deere & Company Service Publications

Fig. 1-6—Spacing the front wheels on a general-purpose tractor.

Experimenters have been working on the development of an external combustion automobile engine for several years.

The Internal Combustion Engine

An internal combustion engine is one in which the fuel is burned and the power is generated within a closed cylinder. All common gasoline or oil-burning engines are of this type.

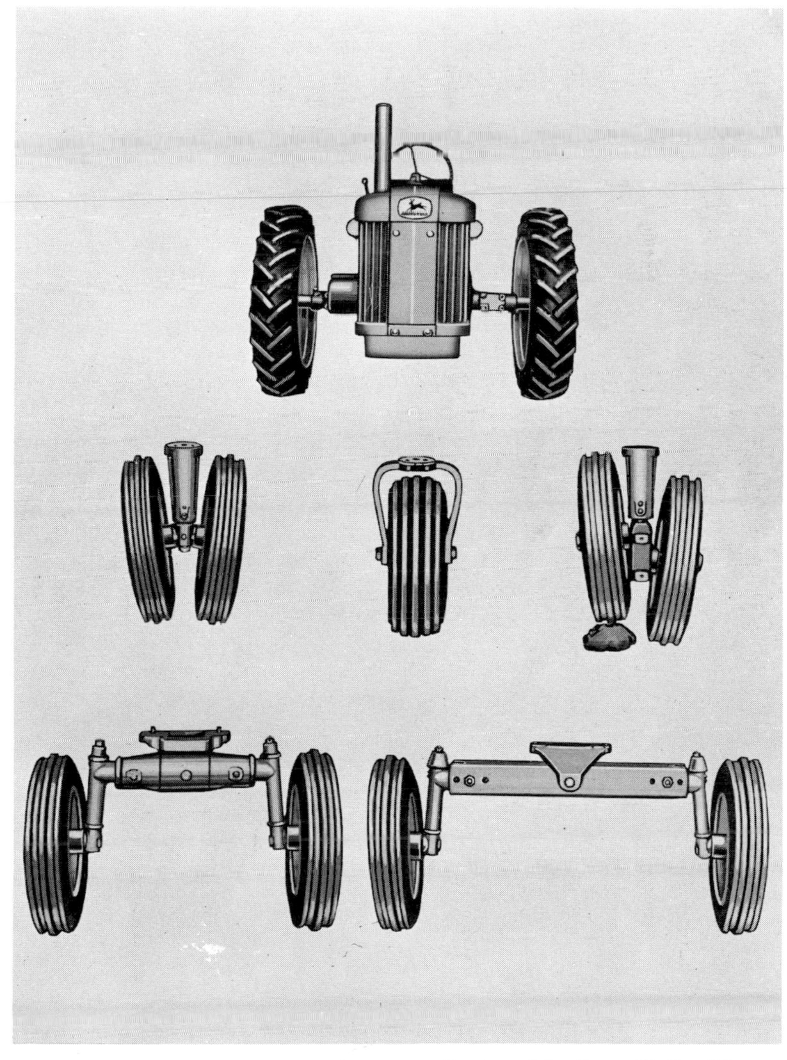

Courtesy John Deere, Moline, Ill.

Fig. 1-7—Available front ends on a general-purpose row-crop tractor.

Courtesy John Deere, Moline, Ill.

Fig. 1-8—A high-clearance row-crop tractor for special crops.

Courtesy Deere & Company Service Publications

Fig. 1-9—Measuring front wheel toe-in.

Principles of Operation

The most common type of gasoline engine is known as the four-stroke cycle (four-cycle) engine. The piston travels the length of the stroke away from the crankshaft twice, and toward the crankshaft twice to produce one power impulse.

Strokes of a Four-Stroke Cycle Engine

1. Intake
2. Compression
3. Power
4. Exhaust

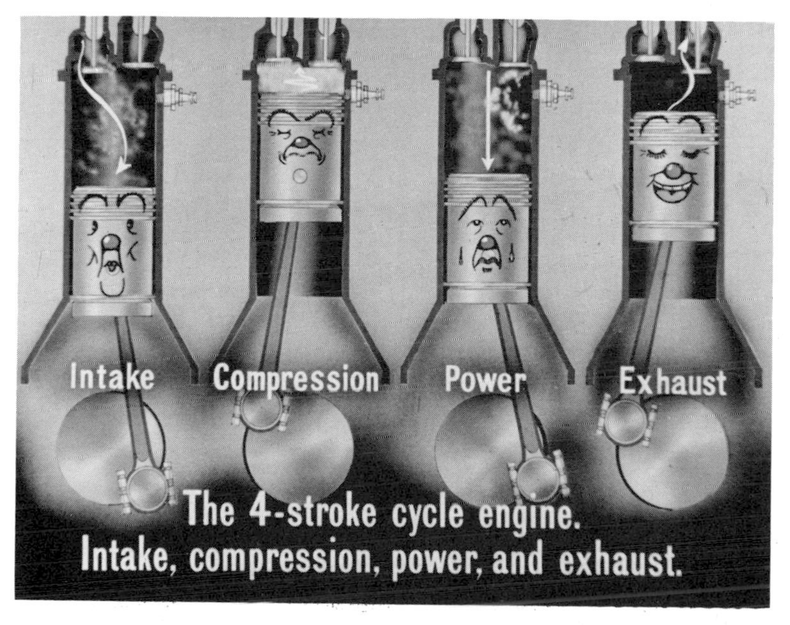

Courtesy John Deere, Moline, Ill.

Fig. 1-10—The strokes of a 4-stroke cycle engine.

Intake Stroke

Fuel is taken into the cylinder from the carburetor through the open intake valve and the intake manifold. This is possible because air rushes through the carburetor and becomes charged with gasoline in finely divided particles as the piston creates a vacuum in the cylinder in moving from the top to the bottom. When the cylinder is filled with this combustible mixture of gasoline and air, the intake valve is closed.

Compression Stroke

When the intake and the exhaust valves are closed, the piston moves from the bottom to the top of the cylinder, compressing the mixture into a small space, known as the combustion chamber.

Before the piston has quite reached the top of the stroke, a spark is introduced and the mixture begins to burn and to expand.

Power Stroke

As the mixture burns, heat is produced. The products of combustion expand because of the heat produced by the burning fuel and push the piston downward on the power stroke.

As the piston nears the bottom of the power stroke the exhaust valve starts to open and becomes fully open by the time the piston is completely down.

Exhaust Stroke

Most of the exhaust gases leave the cylinder with a loud explosive noise. The piston moves upward with the exhaust valve completely open and forces the remaining burned gases out of the cylinder. The exhaust valve is closed shortly after the piston has reached the top of the exhaust stroke and has started down on the intake stroke.

It is possible to close the exhaust valve after the intake stroke has actually started down because of the inertia of gases. It takes a little time to get the incoming gases started to flow into the cylinder, and the exhaust gases will continue to flow out for a short time after the piston quits pushing on them. This allows a better scavenging action. It also has a tendency to keep the combustion chamber from overheating.

Parts of a Gasoline Engine

The preceding actions can take place only because of many interrelated parts, as follows:

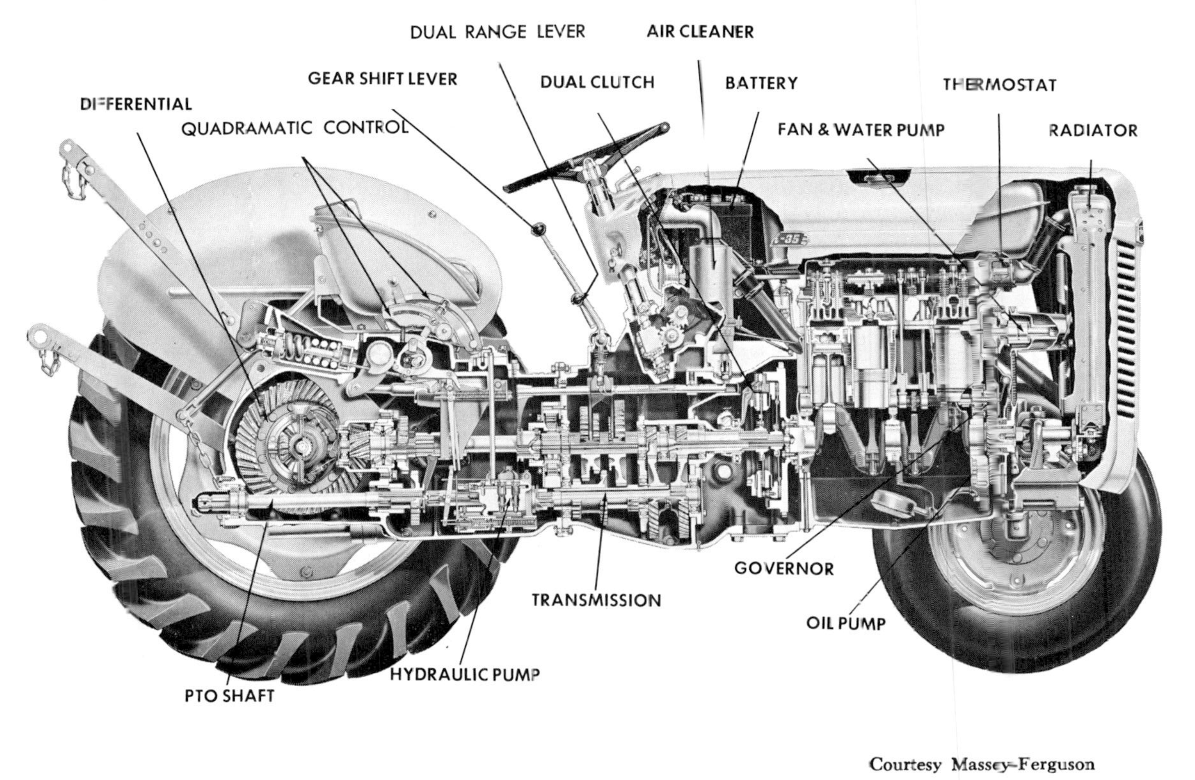

Courtesy Massey-Ferguson

Fig. 1-11—Cutaway view of a small tractor.

1. **Cylinder** in which the
2. **Piston** fits with about 2/1000ths inch space or clearance for expansion and movement.
3. **Piston rings** are fitted into grooves in the piston. They expand against the cylinder wall and tend to make the fit between the piston and cylinder wall gas tight.
4. **Combustion chamber,** formed by the cylinder head and piston, in which is located the
5. **Intake valve** which is so situated that it allows air to be drawn through the
6. **Carburetor** where it picks up gasoline in measured quantities and carries it through the
7. **Intake manifold** into the combustion chamber. Also located here is the
8. **Exhaust valve,** which allows exhaust gases to pass from the cylinder into the open air through an exhaust pipe and muffler.
9. The **connecting rod** is fastened at one end to the piston by means of a
10. **Piston pin,** and at the other end to the
11. **Crankshaft** in such a manner that the power of the burning gases pushing against the piston turns the crankshaft, to which is fastened one or more
12. **Balance wheels** whose function is, partly, to provide the energy to force the piston through the exhaust, intake and compression strokes.

Also located on the crankshaft is a

13. **Timing gear** that meshes with a
14. **Half-time gear** that is usually located on the
15. **Camshaft.** These two gears, sometimes connected by a chain, drive the camshaft upon which is located a cam for each valve, whose function is to open and close the intake and exhaust valves at the proper time.

Also usually driven from the camshaft is the

16. **Ignition system,** either a high tension magneto or a breaker and distributor assembly for battery ignition.
17. An **oil pump** is usually driven from either the crankshaft or camshaft by gears. The oil pump circulates oil throughout the engine
18. Usually a **water pump** and
19. A **cooling fan** are driven from a V-belt pulley on the crankshaft.

If an engine has more than one cylinder the arrangement of the crankshaft, cams and camshaft, intake manifold and ignition system are such that each cylinder functions in relation to every other cylinder to produce an even flow of power.

In order that an engine may perform properly, each of the parts mentioned above must do its job efficiently and in the proper relation to all the jobs performed by all the other parts of the engine.

The engine will run properly and produce the power it should if:

The correct fuel is used;

The right amounts of fuel and air are in the mixture;

The mixture is compressed sufficiently;

The valves open and close at the right time;

The spark is strong and comes at the right time;

The engine runs at the proper temperature;

The correct amount and kind of oil is used;

The oil is changed and filter is serviced regularly.

CLASSIFICATION

Tractor engines may be classified according to the way the fuel is introduced into the cylinder.

Carburetor-Intake Manifold (Spark Ignition)

1. Medium compression, two fuel engines that can be started and warmed up on gasoline, then operated on a lower cost fuel such as distillate or fuel oil. These engines are usually equipped with radiator shutters and manifold heat control valves to aid in the warm-up period and to improve performance on the low cost fuel. Two-fuel tractors are rare except in countries where fuel oil is more available than gasoline.

2. High compression, single fuel engines, burning regular gasoline or liquified petroleum (LP Gas). Gasoline tractors are the most popular, with LP Gas tractors becoming more common in certain areas. Gasoline tractors can be converted to LP Gas operation, but the recommended practice is to purchase factory equipped units.

Diesel (Solid Fuel Injection)

1. Compression ignition, fuel oil engines (diesel), four stroke cycle. The tendency seems to be toward greater use of this type of engine in the larger general-purpose as well as in standard type tractors, with the engine available in some medium size tractors.

2. Compression ignition fuel oil engines (diesel), two stroke cycle. These engines are of a larger scale, very powerful, usually around 70 rated horsepower on the drawbar and are available in the larger standard tread tractors.

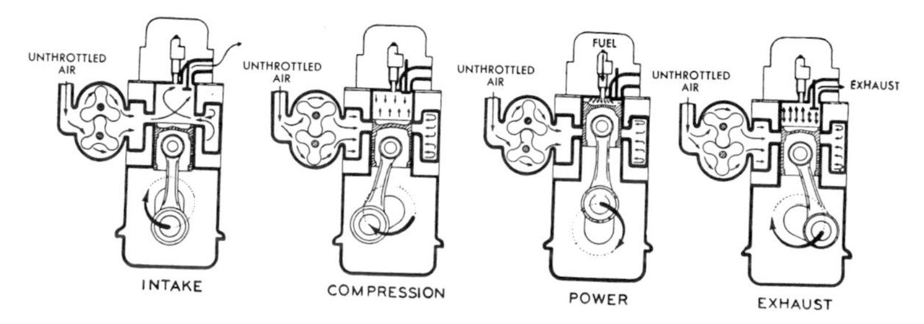

Courtesy Detroit Diesel Engine Div., General Motors Corp.

Fig. 1-12—Operating details of a two-cycle diesel engine with a blower.

Regardless of the type of engine and tractor, the efficiency and amount of use that can be obtained from it will be determined largely by the care and service given to it. Any new machine is tight and needs to be broken-in carefully. The most important period in the life of your tractor is the first 60 to 100 hours. Follow the recommendations in the Operator's Manual carefully during this period.

Courtesy Deere & Company Service Publications

Fig. 1-13—Cutaway view of a turbocharged diesel engine.

THE POWER TRAIN

The remainder of the tractor is as important as the engine but it is not as delicate in its make-up.

To be useful the power produced by the engine must be applied by the traction wheels and tires, or in the belt pulley, or through the power take-off. The line through which power flows in performing useful work is generally known as the power train.

The traction power train consists of clutch, transmission, differential, axles, and wheels or track. The belt-power train generally consists of clutch, bevel pinions, pulley shaft and pulley.

The power take-off power train generally consists of the clutch and power take-off shaft.

THE CLUTCH

The previous statements would indicate that all the useful power that the tractor develops is used through the clutch. The clutch, then, is a very hard working part of the tractor and must be given proper care.

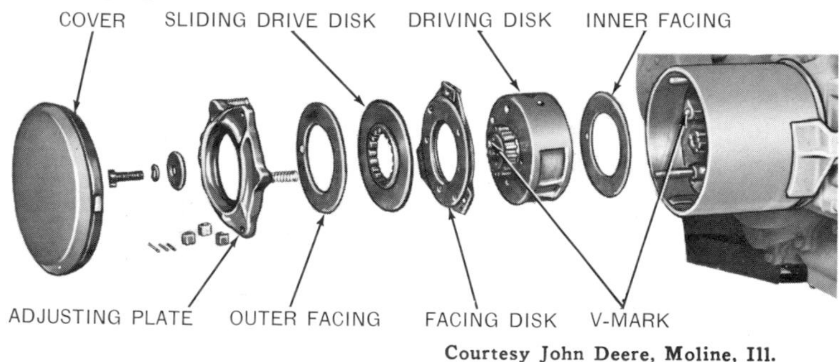

Courtesy John Deere, Moline, Ill.

Fig. 1-14—A hand lever-operated dry plate-type clutch.

Dry plate-type clutches are common on tractors with syncromesh transmissions.

In its more simple form a friction clutch is so constructed that one or more plates or discs driven by the engine contact one or more other discs mounted on a shaft leading to the transmission. The two sets of plates are so constructed that springs exert pressure to hold them together, thus transmitting power from one plate to the other. A clutch release is supplied that separates the plates, allowing the engine to operate freely, without turning any of the remainder of the machinery. Because of the inertia of parts, power must be applied slowly. This is accomplished by engaging the clutch plates slowly and allowing them to slip until inertia is overcome. Continued slipping of the clutch will result in worn or warped plates so that the clutch "grabs" or engages unevenly.

It is very important that the clutch operate freely but without slipping when completely engaged. Keep the clutch pedal free travel adjusted so there is never less than ¾-inch free travel. Check this every 200 hours. Adjust it according to instructions in the Operator's Manual.

In general, the chief care that a clutch needs is to have the throw-out mechanism lubricated according to directions furnished by the manufacturer. In some cases the clutch mechanism is made of materials that do not require lubrication.

THE TRANSMISSION

The transmission is a system of gears so constructed that the mechanical advantage of the engine may be changed with relation to the work to be done and so that direction of movement may be changed. Tractors usually have three or more forward gears as well as a reverse gear in the transmission. These various gears usually allow speeds from about two to seven miles per

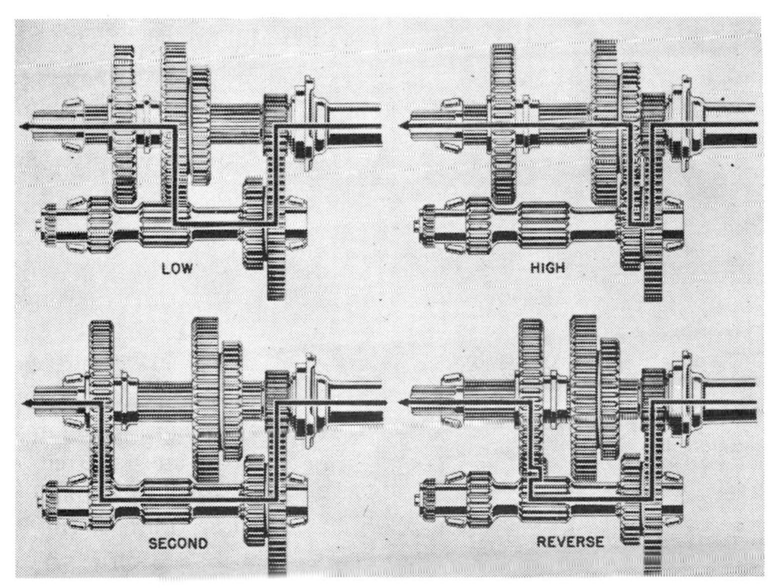

Courtesy Massey-Ferguson

Fig. 1-15—Path of power through the transmission in various gears. Note the location of the sliding gears for each speed.

hour for field work. It may have one or more additional forward gears for road use and it may be able to travel fifteen to twenty or more miles per hour. Care must be taken at the higher speeds to prevent sharp turning which is likely to upset the tractor.

The differential, while not usually considered a part of the transmission, is closely related to it. It is so constructed that one drive-wheel may turn faster or slower than the other. This feature makes it possible for a tractor to turn without one wheel slipping.

Your tractor may be equipped with a differential lock that can be engaged when one wheel starts to slip. This is usually engaged by depressing a foot pedal and disengaged by depressing one or both brake pedals. Do not attempt to turn the tractor when the differential lock is engaged. Always have the front wheels in a straight-ahead position when engaging or disengaging the differential lock.

Courtesy John Deere, Moline, Ill.

Fig. 1-16—A row crop diesel tractor.

The transmission and differential on most tractors are lubricated by the transmission-hydraulic system oil. All bearings and gears are close fitting, and the life of the transmission-hydraulic system depends on keeping the oil level up to the mark, changing the hydraulic system filter as recommended and draining and changing the transmission-hydraulic oil at regular intervals. The oil change interval may vary from 600 to 1,200 hours with different makes of tractor and must not be neglected.

THE POWER TAKE-OFF

The power take-off is merely a shaft extending through the tractor in such a way that connection can be made to it for power to drive machines, such as combines, balers, and other tools which are otherwise powered by drive wheels or independent engines.

Fig. 1-17—Changing from 1,000 RPM to 540 RPM power take-off shaft. Note the number and size of splines on the 540 RPM shaft in the operator's left hand.

The power take-off can be operated with the tractor standing or in motion and most manufacturers now have an arrangement for stopping the forward motion of the tractor without interrupting the power take-off operation. This is very desirable and has led to much greater use of power take-off driven equipment.

New tractors, of the moderate to large size, are equipped so that the new 1000 rpm power take-off shaft may be installed. The new standard speed permits more efficient operation. The 1000 rpm shaft has more, and smaller splines, than the standard 540 shaft. The tractors are designed so that the speed can be changed to correspond to the type shaft being used. The power take-off standards are established by the American Society of Agricultural Engineers (ASAE) and the Society of Automotive Engineers (SAE).

QUESTIONS

1. What is the difference between an external combustion engine and an internal combustion engine?
2. What is the difference between a four-stroke cycle engine and a two-stroke cycle engine?
3. How is the fuel charge ignited in the conventional gasoline engine? How is it ignited in a diesel engine?
4. The intake valve opens at the beginning of what stroke in a four-stroke cycle engine?
5. The exhaust valve opens at the beginning of what stroke?
6. The intake and exhaust valves are closed on what strokes?
7. How fast does the camshaft turn in relation to the crankshaft?
8. How fast does the distributor rotor turn in relation to crankshaft speed, or the distributor rotor makes one revolution to how many revolutions of the crankshaft?
9. Check the procedure for adjusting clutch clearance in several tractor operator's manuals.
10. What are some advantages of a 1000 rpm power take-off shaft speed?

CHAPTER 2

DIESEL ENGINES

Diesel or compression ignition engines are similar to the spark ignition engines in principle. However, there are important differences. On the intake stroke air only enters the cylinder, and is compressed on the next stroke. Compression ratios are extremely high as compared to the conventional engine. At the end of the compression stroke the air temperature has been raised to approximately 1000°F. by decreasing its volume to about 1/16 of the original volume. This temperature is high enough to burn heavy fuel that is sprayed into the compressed and heated air by a specially constructed injection mechanism. Since the diesel engine operates with such high compression, its parts must be heavier and must fit more perfectly than in a spark ignition engine.

Some diesel engines are designed on the two-cycle principle, performing the four necessary operations in two strokes. A blower is usually used to inject air into the cylinder, and to force burned gases out at the end of the power stroke.

The most critical part of the diesel engine is the fuel-injecting system. The plungers are built to fit very closely. Any dust or dirt in the fuel soon wears the injecting pumps until they cannot inject the fuel against the high compression in the cylinder. Special care must be taken with diesel fuel to keep it clean and to deliver it clean to the injecting pumps.

It is interesting to note that when the diesel fuel is injected into the combustion chamber, it must be forced in against a pressure of approximately 600 pounds per square inch. The time available for this fuel injection, in order to time the ignition correctly, is approximately 2 thousandths of a second.

Courtesy American Oil Co.

Fig. 2-1—This farmer uses a filter to help keep his diesel fuel clean.

Fuel storage and methods of handling fuel for diesels will be discussed later. As an added precaution, several very fine screens and filters are used in the supply line. These must be kept clean and operating efficiently as a protection to the pumps.

Manufacturer's instructions are particularly important in servicing diesels.

The maintenance of the diesel engine and the gasoline engine is similar in many respects. The air cleaner, the lubrication, cooling, electrical, hydraulic and power transmission systems are maintained and serviced in about the same way. The fuel and ignition systems are completely different and it is important that these differences be understood. The following is taken from Technical Letter No. X-655, courtesy American Oil Company.

A diesel engine is **not** a gasoline engine.

—Fuel supply to the engine is entirely different.

—Air and fuel mixing is entirely different.

—Ignition is entirely different.

—Engine starting properties of the fuel are entirely different.

—Antiknock properties of the fuel are entirely different.

Diesel fuel properties in lots of ways may be **exactly opposite** to gasoline properties!

Important Opposites

A fuel that gives **Good** starting in a gasoline engine—	Gives **Bad** starting in a diesel.
A fuel that gives **Bad** starting in a gasoline engine—	Gives **Good** starting in a diesel.
A fuel that gives **Good** antiknock in a gasoline engine—	Gives **Bad** antiknock in a diesel.
A fuel that gives **Bad** antiknock in a gasoline engine—	Gives **Good** antiknock in a diesel.

A few things to learn about diesel engines:

The diesel has no intake air throttle.

—Air intake is wide open all the time.

—A full charge of air is taken in on each intake stroke.

The diesel has no carburetor.

—Fuel and air are not mixed before going into the engine.

—Fuel is sprayed into the highly compressed, extremely hot air in a precisely measured small quantity under very high instantaneous pressure at exactly the right time.

The diesel has no electrical spark ignition.

—The fuel spray instantly **self-ignites** as soon as **it hits** the highly heated air. Self-ignition, called "**auto ignition,**" is **not** a matter of volatility.

—No. 2 diesel fuel **auto ignites** faster and at lower temperatures **than a high-octane gasoline!** (We will tell you why a little later.)

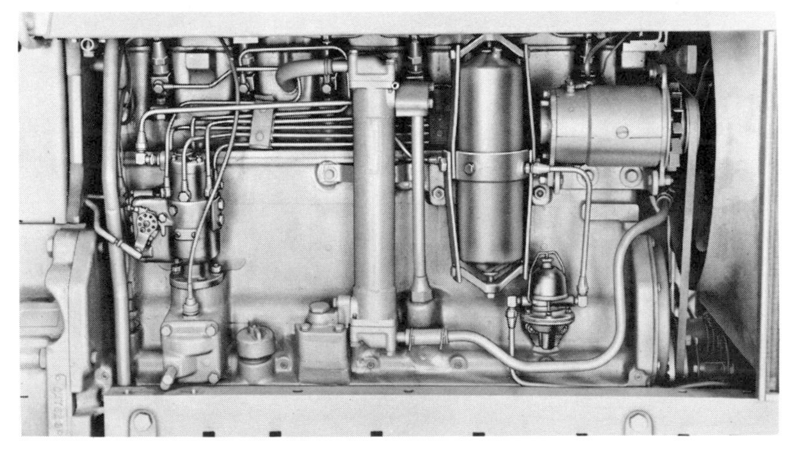

Courtesy John Deere, Moline, Illinois

Fig. 2-2—Fuel system components.

For engines of equal horsepower, the cost of the diesel typically runs from $500 to $1,500 **higher** than the gasoline engine.

–The cost of a typical diesel fuel pumping and injection system alone can run as high as $450 or more.

–Precision fits of pump plungers and injector parts are extremely fine (typically 15-millionths of an inch clearances . . . 1/40th of the thickness of a human hair!) . . . and they are, therefore, costly to make. Particles this small can pass right through the best fuel filters employed.

Don't miss this important point:

Protecting these fine working parts against every possibility of hampering deposits, sediment, rust, or wear is essential to assuring good performance and efficient operation of any diesel engine.

Fuel pump or injector plungers deliver to each cylinder a **precisely** measured quantity of fuel under high pressure.

The variable delivery of the plunger or plungers regulates the power control of the engine–acting like the throttle on a gasoline engine.

The injector delivers the metered fuel into each cylinder employing extremely high pressures applied so fast that the fuel is literally shot into the combustion space as a fine spray. Immediately the fuel spray is self-ignited by the hot, highly compressed air charge.

Correct injector operation is the **key** to good diesel engine operation.

Faulty injector operation is the biggest cause of poor diesel operation.

–Now you know why a diesel requires extra fine filtering to help protect as well as possible the engine's precision-built fuel pumping and injection system.

–Now you know why **fuel quality** is important in any diesel engine.

TURBOCHARGER

A turbocharger is common on many diesel tractors as a part of the intake system. The power developed by an internal combustion engine is determined by the amount of fuel and air which can be packed into each cylinder. More power is developed if more fuel and air can be taken in or packed in by some kind of supercharger. The turbocharger is an exhaust-driven centrifugal-type supercharger driven by a turbine wheel in the exhaust system of the tractor. All the high-pressure exhaust gases from the engine go through the turbine housing, causing the turbine wheel to rotate at a high speed of 40,000 to 100,000 RPM. The turbine spinning in the exhaust stream drives the impeller in the intake

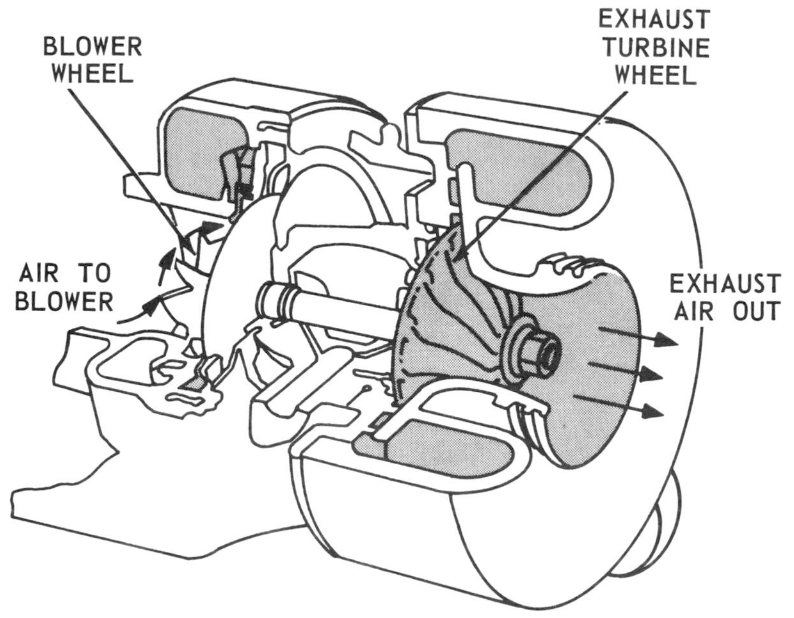

Courtesy John Deere, Moline, Ill.

Fig. 2-3—A cutaway of a turbocharger.

system which takes air from the atmosphere, compresses it and packs it into the engine cylinders. The extremely high speed of the turbine-impeller shaft makes good lubrication of the shaft absolutely essential. The journal bearings and thrust washers on the shaft are usually lubricated with engine oil under pressure.

Courtesy Dana Corp., manufacturer of Perfect Circle Piston Rings

Fig. 2-4—A crack in the hose connecting the turbocharger to the air cleaner. Any leak in the air cleaning system will permit airborne abrasives to enter the engine and cause rapid wear and premature engine failure.

Some special operating instructions should be followed when operating a turbocharged engine because of the high speeds, high temperatures and the need for good lubrication at all times.

1. After starting the engine, wait for positive indication of

oil pressure before increasing the speed of the engine or applying a load.

2. After starting during cold weather, allow the engine to run at least five minutes at half throttle to insure oil pressure at the turbocharger before putting the engine under load.
3. Prime the turbocharger after changing the crankcase oil filter element in the engine, after installing a new or rebuilt turbocharger, after the engine has been idle for a month or more or under any other condition that might allow oil to drain down from the turbocharger bearings. To prime the turbocharger, set the engine speed control lever in the shut-off position, or set the controls so the engine cannot start, and crank the engine until engine oil pressure builds up. Do not crank the engine over 30 seconds at a time.
4. Before stopping the engine, always allow it to idle from three to five minutes to allow heat from the turbocharger and the hot portions of the engine to equalize as the lubricating oil and coolant circulate through the engine. Failure to "cool-out" the engine can damage the turbocharger (as well as the engine) due to distortion and "coking" of oil in the passages.
5. If the engine should stall when operating at normal operating temperature, restart it immediately to prevent damage to the turbocharger. The turbocharger operates at a very high temperature, and if stopped or stalled, oil in the center section may "coke," causing the oil passages to clog. Lack of oil will then cause serious damage or failure of the turbocharger.
6. Cover the exhaust outlet when the engine is not operating to keep out water or other foreign matter. Cover the exhaust outlet when a turbocharged tractor is being transported to keep out foreign matter and to prevent possible rotation of the turbocharger which could damage the shaft bearings due to lack of lubrication.

Cetane Number is a measure of how fast a diesel fuel will **self**-ignite when injected into the engine's combustion spaces.

When the Cetane Number is high enough, your diesel operator will get:

—Good starting.
—Good idling
—Smooth, knock-free operation.

Cetane Number **is opposite** to Octane Number.

In a **gasoline** engine, fuel knock is prevented by the fuel's ability **not** to self-ignite during any part of the burning process. Octane Number is a measure of **this** gasoline property.

In a **diesel** engine, fuel knock is prevented by the fuel's ability to self-ignite fast. Knock and rough running result when there is any appreciable ignition delay. The

Courtesy Allis-Chalmers Corp.

Fig. 2-5—A four-wheel drive articulated tractor with a 218 horsepower V-8 diesel engine developing an estimated 165 horsepower at the drawbar.

lag lets unburned fuel accumulate, finally igniting in a sudden explosion that wastes power and results in rough running. Cetane Number is a measure of a fuel's ability to self-ignite fast. This assures good starting and smooth engine performance.

Cetane is most important during starting. Only indirectly does it affect power output by preventing fuel knock. There is no advantage in using a higher Cetane Number than the engine needs.

QUESTIONS

1. Why are diesel engines usually more efficient than gasoline engines?
2. Why is the compression ratio higher in a diesel engine?
3. What is the main difference in the ignition of diesel and gasoline engines?
4. Why is clean diesel fuel even more important in a diesel engine than clean gasoline in a gasoline engine?
5. Why is it important to follow carefully the instructions in the operator's manual when operating a diesel engine?
6. Where are the fuel and air mixed in a diesel engine?
7. What is the meaning of Cetane Number?
8. How is the speed of a diesel engine controlled since there is no intake air throttle?
9. Why should repair work on the injector system usually be done by a qualified mechanic?
10. What causes fuel knock in a diesel engine?
11. Why should a turbocharged tractor be idled several minutes before being speeded up or placed under a load?
12. Why should the turbocharger be primed on a tractor that has been idle for a month or more or after an oil and filter change?
13. Why should a turbocharged tractor be restarted immediately after it has stalled?

CHAPTER 3

TRACTOR FUELS, OILS AND GREASES

Each internal combustion engine is designed to burn a certain kind of fuel, and for most efficient performance, the proper fuel should always be used. If a fuel that is not correct for the engine is used continually, many difficulties are likely to be experienced: loss of power, over-heating, excessive fuel consumption, knocking, lubrication troubles, rapid wear, and other troubles.

Most tractor engines now operate on gasoline, LP Gas or diesel fuel. Two-fuel engines are available but not used very

Courtesy Deere & Company Service Publications

Fig. 3-1—A good type of farm fuel storage.

widely at the present. These engines are designed to be warmed up on gasoline and then operated on a heavier fuel.

The operator's manual should be consulted for the manufacturer's recommendation on the proper fuel to use for different operating conditions. This is especially important for diesel engines.

Certain facts about fuels and engines should be understood to enable the operator to select satisfactory fuels for his engine. These are discussed in the following pages.

ENGINE CHARACTERISTICS

Compression Ratio

The compression ratio is the relationship between the volume of the fuel and air mixture (combustible mixture) in the cylinder when the piston is at the bottom and the volume of the same combustible mixture when the piston is at the top of the stroke.

If the volume of combustible mixture in a cylinder when the piston is at the bottom of the stroke is 72 cubic inches, and the mixture is compressed to a volume of 12 cubic inches when the piston is at the top of the stroke, the compression ratio is 6 to 1. The significance of the compression ratio of an engine can be more fully understood if one remembers that the amount of pressure on the piston determines the power of the engine. Other things being equal, the greater the pressure at the beginning of the power stroke, the greater will be the power developed.

It will be seen that, as the compression ratio increases, the power output increases. Generally speaking, this is true. However, practical application of this principle has been found difficult beyond certain points. Designers and experimenters are working to increase the compression ratio and hence the power output of engines, beyond what is economically possible at this time.

Increasing the compression ratio, and increasing safe operating speeds of engines has, in the past few years, reduced the weight of engines by nearly one-third and the piston displace-

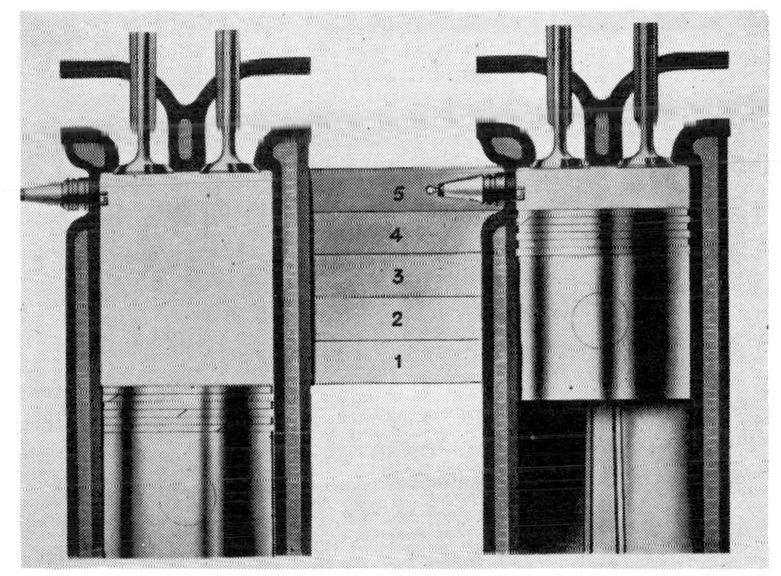

Courtesy Ethyl Corp.

Fig. 3-2—Picturization of a 5:1 compression ratio.

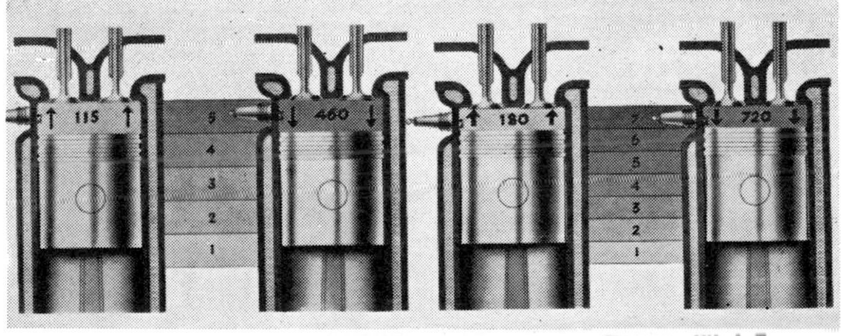

Courtesy Ethyl Corp.

Fig. 3-3—Comparison of compression pressures and combustion pressures in low and high compression engines. Note that an increase in **compression** pressure of 65 lbs. (from 115 to 180) results in an increase in **combustion** pressure of 260 lbs. This represents a real increase in efficiency.

ment by more than one-half. This improvement has also increased fuel economy.

Compression ratio is directly related to the kind of fuel that can be used without knocking. As the compression ratio goes up, the tendency to knock increases.

Detonation

Detonation has been variously explained as "spark knock," "pre-ignition," "carbon knock," etc. Research into detonation shows that it is the result of many factors, chief of which are the following:

(1) Chemical composition of fuel.
(2) Compression ratio.
(3) Ignition timing.
(4) Mixture ratio.
(5) Water-jacket temperature.
(6) Mixture temperature.
(7) Working conditions—load, speed, etc.

All of the above factors must be kept properly related to avoid trouble and inefficiency in an engine. Most of the above factors are more or less under the control of the operator. It is the operator's responsibility to control these factors if he would obtain the utmost in trouble-free operation.

Continued operation of an engine that knocks because one or more of the factors mentioned above is not controlled may result in burned valves and pistons, break-down of cylinder lubrication, burned-out head gaskets, and ruined spark plugs, to say nothing of wasted fuel, lack of power, and continued annoyance. Engines have been known to become severely damaged in a short time because of detonation.

FUELS

Present day internal combustion engine fuels are practically all produced from petroleum, or crude oil. Petroleum molecules are made up of hydrogen and carbon atoms joined together in many different patterns forming literally thousands of different molecules. Our gasoline at one time came from the crude oil as

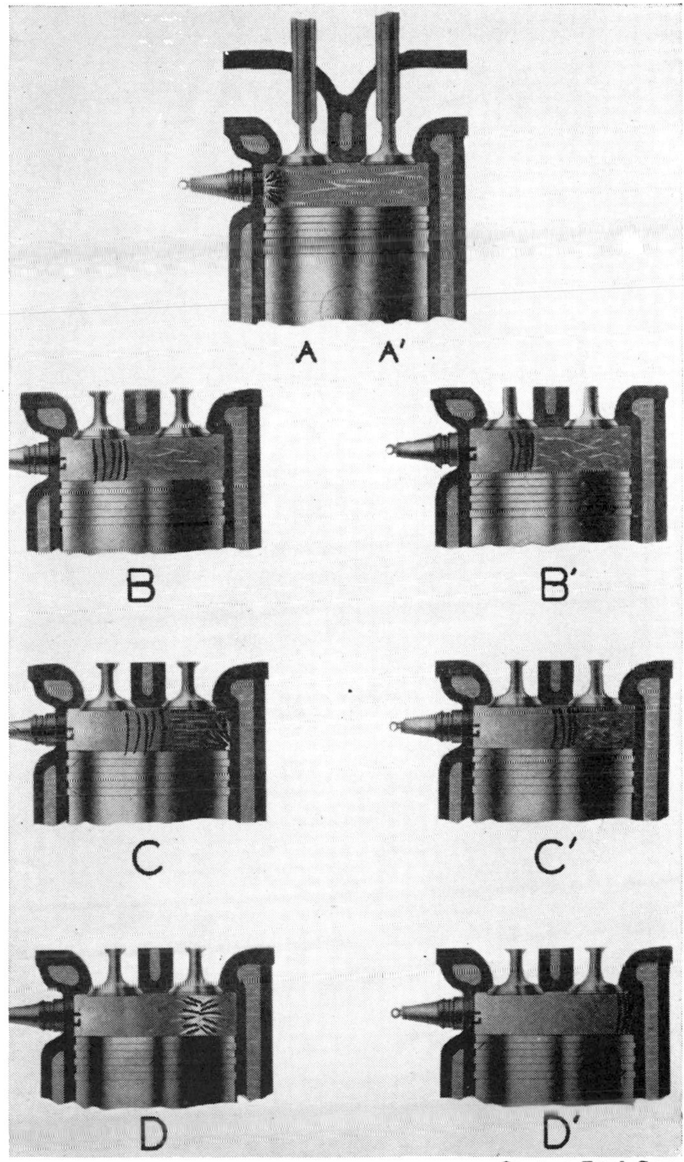

Courtesy Ethyl Corp.

Fig. 3-4—Illustrating how detonation may occur A, B, C, D as low octane fuel burns, as compared to no detonation B[1], C[1], D[1] when high octane fuel is burned.

a result of a simple distillation process. This process could not possibly supply the fuel required at the present time by the millions of engines in operation. Fortunately, the oil scientists have discovered ways of cracking the oil molecules and recombining them in such a way as to more than double the yield of gasoline from crude oil, at the same time improving the quality of gasoline obtained. This improvement in quality has aided in making possible the development of the modern high compression engine.

LIQUID FUEL CHARACTERISTICS

Liquid fuels are composed of parts that vaporize at different temperatures. Those parts that vaporize at the lower temperatures heat up the other parts as they burn, resulting in a progressive burning of the fuel charge. Gasoline is blended to give good starting and warm up characteristics for the season in which it is sold and for the section of the country in which it will be used. This feature should be kept in mind when buying gasoline and indicates that large quantities should not be stored on the farm for long periods.

Burning a charge of liquid fuel may be compared in some respects, to building a solid fuel fire. This might be done by putting the large solid chunks of fuel in the bottom of the fire box, with the smaller, lighter material next, with the kindling on top, covering this with shavings and paper. The match is applied to the paper which ignites the shavings, which in turn ignites the kindling, and so on until the heavy fuel is burning.

Much the same thing happens with a charge of liquid fuel in a cylinder. The comparison may be more meaningful if the heavier ends of the liquid fuel (those parts that vaporize at about 330° F. to 400° F.) are considered as the heavy chunks of the solid fuel, the medium ends (those that vaporize at about 230° to 330°) as the finer material, the light ends (those that vaporize at about 100° to 200°) as shavings, and the initial boiling point light end as the paper. Then the match flame becomes the spark, and the fire is kindled.

In a typical summer grade of gasoline, the initial boiling

point would be about 97°, 10% would be vaporized at 135°, 50% at 230°, 90% at 333° and the end point would be at 395°.

Such an arrangement tends to insure that all the fuel will be burned. If all of the liquid fuel were to evaporate at one temperature, it is doubtful whether all of it could be burned in the time it would have in which to burn. Thus fuel would be wasted.

Anti-Knock Fuels

Engineers early realized that better fuels were needed to aid in the development of the internal combustion engine. Among other things, a fuel must be able to work under high compressions without knocking. Many scientists and engineers have attacked the problem and have found several solutions, some of which were practical.

Gasoline in common use is satisfactory in our modern engines largely because of two developments:

(1) Cracking.

Gasoline was originally a product of the simple distillation of crude oil, and the gasolines produced by various manufacturers varied greatly. As more and more gasoline was needed, a process of distilling crude oil and its usual products under heat and pressure was developed. Gasoline thus made proved to be able to work under higher compression than the former straight-run gasolines. In addition, much more gasoline could be produced from the same amount of crude oil.

The cracking process made possible certain improvement in engines, which resulted in more work per gallon of fuel and a wider acceptance of internal combustion engines.

(2) Additives.

Chemists and engineers discovered that certain materials could be added to gasoline that would enable them to operate under higher compressions than could cracked gasolines alone. Alcohol was one additive that gave good results, but it proved somewhat unsatisfactory in actual use.

A compound known as "Tetra Ethyl Lead" has had a wide distribution as an anti-knock additive. This material when added to gasoline in proper amounts allows it to perform satisfactorily in high compression engines.

Octane Number or Rating

In order to standardize the anti-knock characteristics of fuels, it was necessary to have a measuring device. Accordingly scientists more or less arbitrarily decided that because of their actions in a test engine, normal heptane, a hydrocarbon fuel would have zero anti-knock characteristics, and that iso-octane, another hydrocarbon fuel, would have 100 anti-knock characteristics.

These two fuels, mixed in varying proportions would form the basis for comparing commercial fuels. The procedure for determining the anti-knock rating or octane number of a fuel is to operate it in a test engine, the performance of which can be measured accurately, and then to mix heptane and iso-octane until it duplicates the performance of the commercial fuel. For example, if it requires 83 parts of iso-octane and 17 parts of normal heptane to duplicate the performance of the fuel in question, it is said that the fuel has an octane rating of 83.

DIESEL FUEL

Diesel tractor fuel used in farm tractors is available in two grades: Grade No. 1-D and Grade No. 2-D.

Grade No. 1-D comprises the class of fuel oils from kerosene to the intermediate distillates. Fuels within this classification are applicable for use in high-speed engines in services involving frequent and relatively wide variations in loads and speeds, and also for use in cases where abnormally low fuel temperatures are encountered.

Grade No. 2-D includes the class of distillate gas oils of lower volatility. These fuels are applicable for use in high-speed engines in services involving relatively high loads and uniform speeds, or in engines not requiring fuels having the higher volatility or other properties specified for Grade No. 1-D.

In a typical Grade No. 1-D fuel, the initial boiling point would be about 366°, 10% would be vaporized at 413°, 50% at 466°, 90% at 530° and the end point would be at 574°.

In a typical Grade No. 2-D fuel, the initial boiling point would be about 376°, 10% would be vaporized at 440°, 50% at 509°, 90% at 592° and the end point would be at 653°.

CETANE NUMBER

The ignition quality of diesel fuels is indicated in terms of cetane number. Blends of two hydrocarbons are used in determining the cetane number of a fuel. Cetane is a hydrocarbon with very high ignition quality and was chosen to represent the top of the scale with a cetane number of 100. The hydrocarbon called alphamethylnaphthalene has very low ignition quality and was chosen to represent the bottom of the scale with a cetane number of zero. Blends of these two fuels represent intermediate ignition quality and their cetane number is the percentage of cetane in the blend. For example, a reference fuel blend containing 40 percent cetane and 60 percent alphamethylnaphthalene is assigned a cetane number of 40.

A sample of fuel whose cetane number is to be determined is tested in a special single-cylinder engine. If the sample fuel has the same ignition qualities as a reference fuel with a 40 cetane number, the sample is designated a 40 cetane number fuel.

The relationship between the cetane number of a diesel fuel and the performance of a diesel engine should not be confused with the relationship between gasoline octane number and spark-ignition engine performance. In a gasoline engine, the higher the octane number the greater the potential engine performance because of the possibility of increased compression ratio or supercharging, and the octane number requirement is determined by the full-load demand of the engine. In case of a diesel engine, the desirable level of cetane number is established by the requirements for good ignition quality at light loads and low temperatures.

Cetane Number is a measure of how fast a diesel fuel will self-ignite when injected into the engine's combustion spaces.

STORING FUEL

Storing fuel on the farm becomes a problem affecting tractor maintenance when we consider that the operating efficiency and life of the tractor are greatly influenced by the quality and cleanliness of the fuel placed in the tractor fuel tank. It is possible to purchase high quality, clean fuel and find, later, that the fuel being used to fill the tractor fuel tank is contaminated and low in quality because of poor storage and handling facilities on the farm. We shall consider, here, the problems encountered in storing gasoline, LP Gas and diesel fuel.

Courtesy American Oil Co.

Fig. 3-5—Poor farm fuel storage and handling equipment. A good way to get dirt in the fuel when funnels and cans are left outside.

STORING GASOLINE

Of the three fuels being considered, gasoline is probably the most difficult to store successfully on the farm. Several things happen to gasoline in storage; it evaporates and decreases in quality, the gum content increases, water gets into the tank by condensation, and when it is finally used it does not burn readily and warms the engine slowly.

Let us consider ways of storing gasoline so that evaporation loss is decreased, quality is maintained and fire hazards are reduced.

The underground tank is satisfactory for maintaining quality because there is little change in temperature resulting in less evaporation and less condensation of moisture in the tank.

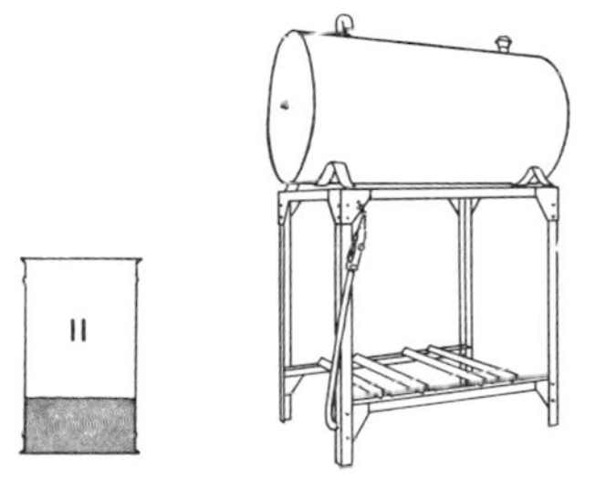

11 gallons lost from vented 290 gallon tank.

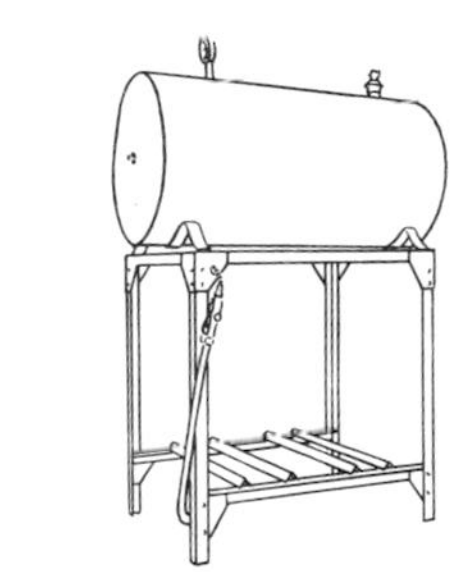

3 gallons lost from 290 gallon tank with pressure maintained at 3 psi.

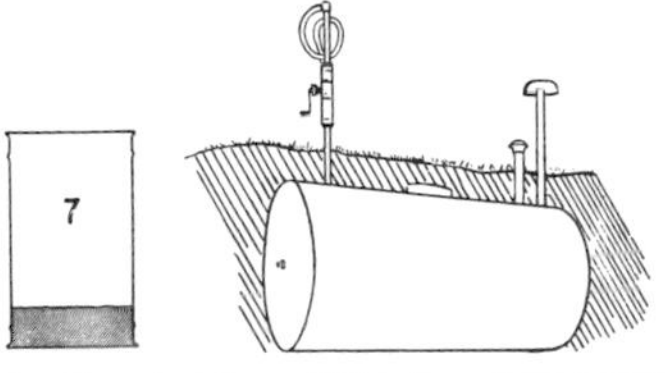

7 gallons lost from 290 gallon underground tank.

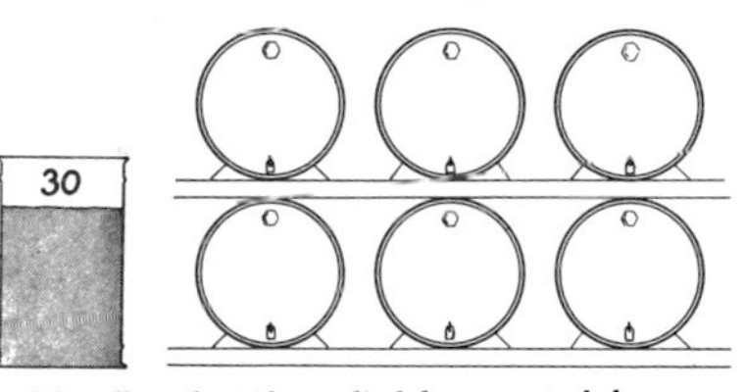

30 gallons lost if supplied from vented drums.

Courtesy Purdue University Cooperative Extension Service

Fig. 3-6—The type of fuel storage used makes a big difference. The above losses were observed in one series of tests where a 200 gallon average supply of gasoline was maintained and 200 gallons were withdrawn per month.

A relatively new method of maintaining quality is to use a pressure cap on an above-ground tank. Several companies now have these caps on the market. The cap ordinarily consists of two valves, one is spring loaded to permit pressure in the tank to build up to about 3 pounds per square inch (psi). The other valve is spring loaded, so that when the tank cools and there is a slight negative pressure, air may enter and equalize the pressure.

Gasoline is a perishable product. Anything that can be done to reduce evaporation losses and keep the fuel cool is a good practice.

Pressurized storage can be accomplished by installing a pressure cap at the filler opening as described above. The cap must have a vacuum release valve to equalize the pressure when the tank cools. On tanks having a separate vent pipe, the pipe must be sealed when the pressure cap is installed.

Courtesy Purdue University Cooperative Extension Service

Fig. 3-7—Installation of this pressure cap on a farm tank requires use of a 16″ pipe wrench. A padlock may be attached in the holes through the flange. Before filling a tractor gas tank the pressure may be relieved by pressing the vacuum release valve.

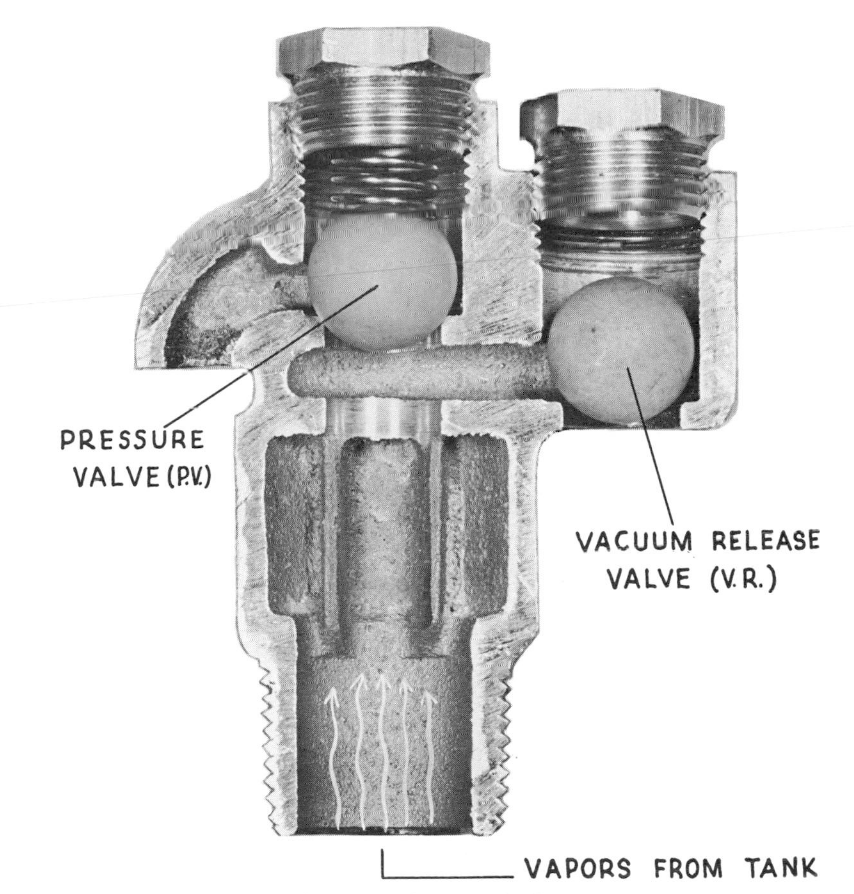

Courtesy Purdue University Cooperative Extension Service

Fig. 3-8—The necessary components to pressurize a fuel storage tank. A typical day's operational cycle might be as follows:

MORNING—Gasoline temperature rises, vapor pressure starts to increase. Vapors retained by spring tension on P.V. Pressure tends to hold V.R. on its seat. No vapor escape.

AFTERNOON—Vapor pressure rises until it exceeds the spring tension. P.V. opens to allow escape of enough vapor to return pressure to 3 P.S.I.

NIGHT—Gasoline cools, vapor pressure decreases to zero and vacuum is formed. At slight negative pressure, V.R. opens, allowing air to enter and equalize pressure.

FILLING TRACTOR TANK—Air will enter through V.R. when withdrawing fuel from the tank.

The installation of a pressure cap will reduce evaporation losses, save the light ends of the fuel for cold weather starting and quick warm up, reduce gum formation and crankcase oil dilution.

Locating tanks in deep shade will aid in cutting evaporation losses and condensation.

SAFETY RECOMMENDATIONS FOR GASOLINE

1. Keep fire and flame away from gasoline.
2. Turn engine off before refueling, if possible refuel when engine has cooled.
3. When refueling, make certain hose nozzle is in constant metal-to-metal contact with the tank being filled. Under certain conditions static electricity will fire the fumes.

Courtesy John Deere, Moline, Ill.

Fig. 3-9—Never smoke around the tractor when filling the fuel tank.

4. Elevated tanks:
   a. Make certain of stability of tank supports.
   b. Equip and maintain internal check valve at tank outlet.
   c. Equip and maintain self-closing valve at discharge end of tank. This valve will close automatically in case of fire.
5. Tanks with opening in top:
   a. If on ground, support bottom of tank on timbers or blocks to prevent corrosion.
   b. Use tight, permanently attached pumping device.
   c. Include an effective anti-syphoning device in the pump discharge.
6. Provide a lock for the tank valve; children may play with this valve.
7. Be sure above-ground tanks *are grounded* for lightning protection.
8. Locate the tank 50 feet away from any building or other fire hazard. Locating closer than 15 feet may void the fire insurance on a building.
9. Mark the tank: (Inflammable—Keep Fire & Flame Away).
10. Identify the fuel in the tank: "G" for gasoline, "D" for diesel fuel.
11. Stop leaks in the tank or hose.
12. Stop leaks in the tractor fuel line or carburetor.
13. Don't fill the storage tank too full, allow room for expansion.
14. Don't fill the tractor tank too full.
15. If fuel splashes out of the tractor tank, get a new cap; you may burn up your tractor.

STORING DIESEL FUEL

The importance of proper handling and storage of diesel fuel cannot be emphasized too strongly. Many of the difficulties with diesel engine operation can be traced to dirt in the fuel. To keep fuel injection equipment in efficient operating condition all scale, dirt, lint and water must be kept out of the fuel.

DIESEL FUEL STORAGE AND HANDLING SUGGESTIONS

Store fuel in a convenient place outside of buildings.

A storage tank with a pump and drain is the best means of storing fuel.

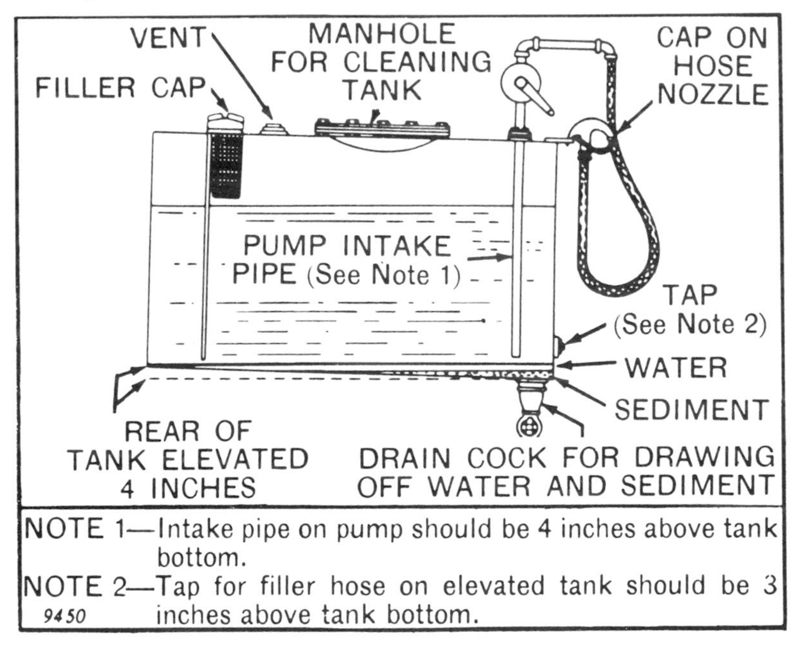

Fig. 3-10—One type of fuel storage tank.

After the tank is filled, allow 24 to 48 hours for water and sediment to settle before withdrawing fuel for the tractor.

Have the tank firmly anchored on a strong platform for stability.

Drain water and sediment from the tank frequently.

The hose nozzle should be capped when not in use to keep dust out.

If a container is used to carry fuel from the storage tank to the tractor, keep it clean with a cover and flush it out with some fuel before use.

Barrels are not recommended for fuel storage.

If barrels are used, keep the rear end of the barrel lower so that water and dirt will settle at the rear and not be drawn out of the spigot.

Place barrels in such a position that they will not have to be moved before withdrawing the fuel.

Do not try to remove all the fuel from a tank or barrel for the purpose of filling the tractor fuel tank. Empty the remaining fuel into a container and let it settle out before using it.

Store barrels under shelter to prevent water from getting into them.

If barrels must be used for storage, provide enough barrels to allow sufficient time for settling.

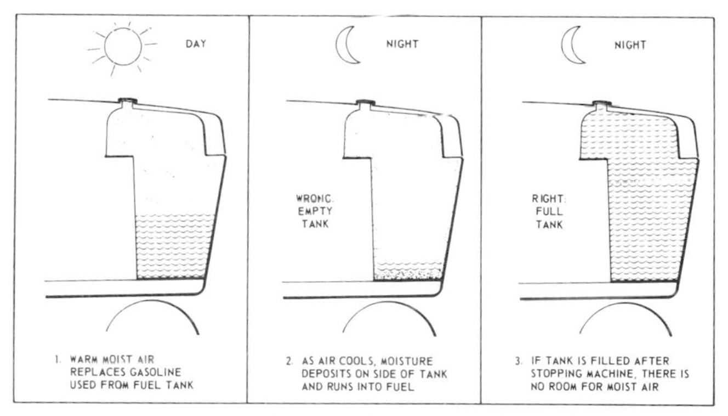

Courtesy Deere & Company Service Publications

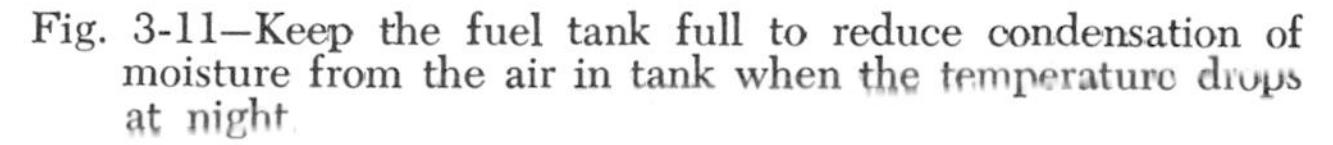

Fig. 3-11—Keep the fuel tank full to reduce condensation of moisture from the air in tank when the temperature drops at night.

The tractor fuel tank should be filled at the end of the day's run, after the tractor has cooled. This will reduce condensation by reducing the air space in the tank.

Don't mix other fuels with diesel fuel.

Courtesy John Deere, Moline, Ill.

Fig. 3-12—An approved above ground storage tank for LP Gas.

STORING LP GAS

LP Gas under moderate pressure becomes liquid and is handled and shipped in the liquid state. In the gaseous state this fuel presents hazards common to other types of gases, except that it is heavier than air and will collect in low places in case there is a leak in a storage tank or fuel transfer device. It is well to follow the recommendations of the supplier in storing and handling LP Gas. If these recommendations are followed, the fuel should be no more dangerous to handle than gasoline.

Liquefied Petroleum Gas Storage

Above ground tanks are recommended for LP Gas to enable the detection of leaks. This fuel is under very high pressures and thus requires carefully installed facilities.

Tanks with Underwriters Laboratories' approval label should be purchased. The most important consideration in the installation of one of these containers, which is to serve a house as well as vehicles, is its foundation. Freezing and thawing causes movement of the tank if not on a deep foundation. This movement may crack the fittings to the tank and allow the gas to escape.

The vapors of this fuel are heavier than air. They will settle in low spots on the ground or in a building and thus create an explosive mixture. An artificial odor is manufactured into LP Gas for the detection of leaks. Soap suds are another effective method to check connections. **Never use flame for leak detection.**

Storage tanks for LP Gas should be located at least 50 feet from buildings or property lines.

LP Gas fuel tanks should never be filled 100 percent full. A 10 percent to 20 percent vapor space must be allowed for expansion of the fuel with temperature increases.

from Purdue University Extension Leaflet 367

SAFETY PRECAUTIONS

1. Operate engine in well ventilated areas.
2. Engine and fuel system repair work should be done in well ventilated area to avoid low pockets such as unventilated pits.
3. Don't store vehicles over unventilated pits (garaging).
4. Shut off fuel tank valve and run engine out of fuel before doing engine work.
5. Avoid open flames near repair work, use danger signs and prohibit smoking in area.
6. Ventilate engine compartment after servicing.
7. On accident vehicles, check for leaks before inside storage.
8. Work on fuel tank should be done by specialized people.
9. Never use LP Gas for cleaning parts, blowing horns, inflating tires, cleaning out cab and other uses not intended for LP Gas and where there is no control of the fuel.
10. After repairs check for leaks—by smell or soapy water. NEVER A FLAME.
11. If possible use a vapor return line when refueling.

12. Do not replace high pressure fittings with other than high pressure parts.
13. Fuel system should have a safety shut-off controlled by engine ignition switch.
14. Have CO_2 or dry powder fire extinguisher available.
15. Never vent fuel system in an enclosed area.
16. Drain the fuel system prior to storing vehicles for extended periods.

Courtesy of Texaco's magazine LUBRICATION

ENGINE LUBRICATING OILS

There have been many important changes and improvements in lubricating oils in recent years. These improvements have been made to meet the lubrication needs of the modern high performance engine and are a result of close association and cooperation between the petroleum industry and engine manufacturers.

The engine crankcase oil has at least five main functions to perform:

- **It reduces friction between moving parts in the engine.**
- **It reduces wear as much as possible.**
- **It lubricates cylinder walls and piston rings and forms a seal between them.**
- **It absorbs heat and helps conduct it to the cooling system.**
- **It acts as a cushion to absorb shock loads and helps deaden engine noise.**

The straight mineral oil used several years ago cannot adequately perform all these functions, so the high quality modern oil is a blend of lubricating oil and chemicals called additives. One of these additives is a detergent and this gives us the popular term, detergent oil. A modern top quality motor oil may contain a combination of the following additives:

1. **Detergent-dispersant additive** helps keep metal surfaces clean and keeps deposit-forming materials dispersed throughout the oil so they may be drained out with the old oil.

Particles of soot and oxidized oil or fuel are so fine they pass through the oil filter and continue to be carried by the oil until drained. Black oil indicates that an oil is helping keep the engine clean by carrying combustion particles, rather than letting them accumulate in the engine as sludge.

2. **Oxidation inhibitor additive** helps keep the oil from oxidizing at high temperatures. Helps prevent acid, sludge and varnish formations. Protects alloy bearings from corrosion.
3. **Anti-corrosion additive** helps prevent damage to alloy bearings from corrosive acids formed as a natural by-product of combustion. Protects other metal surfaces from corrosion and works with the oxidation inhibitor.
4. **Anti-rust additive** prevents rusting of metal parts during storage periods or over weekends when the tractor is not used. Neutralizes acids to make them less harmful. Forms a protective coating on metal surfaces.
5. **Foam inhibitor additive** helps keep the oil from foaming as it circulates rapidly by speeding the rate at which air bubbles break up.
6. **Pour point depressant additive** prevents wax crystals from congealing in extremely cold temperatures to interfere with oil flow and adequate lubrication.
7. **Extreme pressure additive** assures lubrication between close-fitting parts under extreme pressure to prevent metal-to-metal contact. This reduces friction and helps prevent galling, scoring, seizure and abnormal wear.
8. **Viscosity index improver additive** makes possible multi-viscosity oils that span a wide range of viscosity grades compared to single viscosity oils. Lighter oils give good lubrication and aid in starting at lower temperatures. Heavier oils give good lubrication and protection at high temperatures but thicken and cause hard starting and improper lubrication at low temperatures. The multi-viscosity oils have beneficial properties of both light and heavy oils.

CHOOSING LUBRICATING OIL

The operator's choice of lubricating oil may seriously affect the useful life of the tractor engine. There are two very important factors to be considered when selecting lubricating oil for any engine. One is the SAE viscosity or weight of oil to use for the anticipated air temperature, and the other is the quality as indicated by the new API Engine Service Classification System.

VISCOSITY

SAE viscosity numbers classify oils according to viscosity only and indicate nothing about quality or serviceability of the oil. The classification simply means that at certain specified temperatures a certain amount of oil will run through a certain sized hole in a certain number of seconds.

Lubricating oils are available with the following SAE single viscosity numbers: 5W, 10W, 20W, 20, 30, 40, 50. Single viscosity oil is usually recommended for heavy duty diesel engines.

Multi-viscosity oil is available in many SAE numbers such as: 5W-20, 10W-20, 10W-30, 10W-40, 20W-40, 10W-50. These oils span several SAE single viscosity classifications. Multi-viscosity oils are widely used in automobiles, trucks and spark ignition tractor engines operating under low temperature conditions. For tractor engines operating in typical summer temperatures, a single viscosity oil is usually recommended.

A 10W-30 multi-viscosity oil has the low temperature viscosity of a 10W oil and the high temperature viscosity of an SAE 30

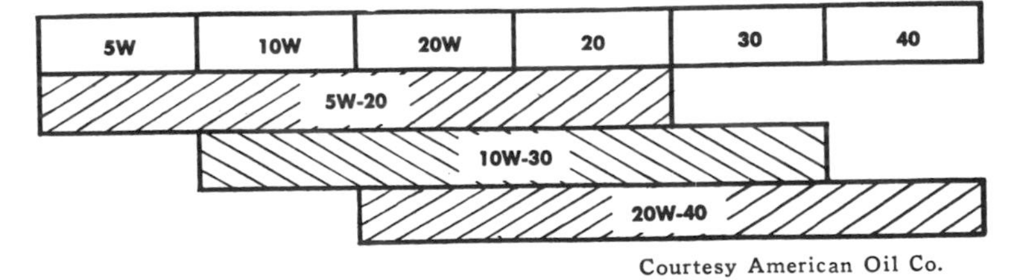

Courtesy American Oil Co.

Fig. 3-13—Overlap comparison of single viscosity and multi-viscosity oils.

oil. The addition of viscosity index improvers to the oil by the oil company makes possible the multi-viscosity oil.

A multi-viscosity oil permits easier starting in cold weather and better lubrication during the warm-up period when most engine wear is likely to take place. The manufacturer's recommendation should be followed when substituting multi-viscosity oil for single viscosity oil.

QUALITY

Until recently, the tractor operator had to depend on the reliability of the manufacturer in selecting the quality of oil to use in an engine. He should still depend on reputable manufacturers, but there is now available a designation that may be used in determining the oil to use for the type of service under which the engine will be operated. This designation is the API (American Petroleum Institute) Engine Service Classifications.

The American Petroleum Institute in 1947 adopted a system which designated crankcase oils as: Regular type, Premium type, and Heavy Duty type. Generally, the Regular type oils were straight mineral oils; Premium type oils contained oxidation inhibitors; and Heavy Duty type oils contained oxidation inhibitors, plus detergent-dispersant additives.

This oil-type classification system did not recognize that gasoline and diesel engines might have different crankcase oil requirements or that the engine requirements would be affected by engine operating conditions, composition of the fuel and other factors. It became evident to both the oil and engine manufacturers that the recognized oil-type definitions were inadequate. As a result, the Lubrication Subcommittee of the American Petroleum Institute, cooperating with the American Society for Testing and Materials, developed a new system of Engine Service Classification in 1952 which was revised in 1955 and again in 1960.

This API Engine Classification System described and classified, in general terms, the service conditions under which engines were operated. The system included three service classifications for gasoline engines (ML, MM and MS) and three for diesel engines (DG, DM and DS).

While this system was a great improvement over the earlier system, it eventually became apparent that more effective means of communicating engine oil performance and engine service classification information between engine manufacturers, the petroleum industry and the customer was required.

Accordingly in 1969 and 1970 the American Petroleum Institute (API), the American Society for Testing and Materials (ASTM) and the Society of Automotive Engineers (SAE) cooperated in establishing an entirely new classification system. SAE determined that there were eight separate categories of automotive type engine oils of current substantial commercial interest. ASTM established the test methods and performance characteristics and technically described each of the categories (ASTM Research Report RR D2:1002 January 1970). API prepared a "user" language, including new engine service letter designations for each of the eight different operating conditions for which the eight different types of engine oil were suited. These eight engine service classifications were correlated to the ASTM technical descriptions and primary performance criteria. SAE then published the entire project result as SAE Recommended Practice J 183.

Late in 1970, a ninth class of service was added to reflect the anticipated service requirements of new model automobiles. This addition is technically described in the January 1971 revision to ASTM Research Report RR D2:1002.

In devising the API Engine Service Classification System, it was recognized that the satisfactory performance of internal combustion engines is dependent mainly on a suitable combination of the following factors:

Engine Design and Construction
Fuel
Operating Conditions
Lubricating Oil
Maintenance Practices

These factors fix the lubrication requirements of an engine.

Engine design and construction vary widely in accordance with the emphasis placed by individual engine manufacturers on different features of design and construction.

Fuels, especially diesel fuels, also differ, depending upon the crude oil and the refining method used.

Operating conditions of engines vary from operation under light or intermittent load, often accompanied by prolonged idling, to extreme overloading; and from driving at low or moderate speeds to continuous high-speed operation. Ambient temperatures may range from subzero cold to desert heat.

Lubricating oil characteristics and performance depend on the crude oil source, refining methods used, base stocks selected and the additives which may be incorporated in the finished oils by the manufacturers. Since engine design and operating conditions are so variable, oils are made with different performance properties, some being suitable only for the lightest service, others for a wider range of service.

Maintenance practices of engines vary. Despite good engine design, favorable operating conditions and the use of the best fuels and lubricants, unsatisfactory performance will occur from faulty carburetor adjustment; lack of periodic engine tune-ups; improper thermostatic control; improper operation of positive crankcase ventilation (PCV) systems, exhaust and other emission control devices; extended oil drain and oil filter replacement intervals; and failure to maintain clean air filters.

The new API Engine Service Classification System continues to define and explain classes of service for both diesel and gasoline engine applications. It provides a means of identifying service requirements with oil performance from a lubrication standpoint. These requirements range from the mildest requiring minimum protection against deposits, wear or rust to the severe requirements imposed on automotive gasoline engines by:

Short trip, start-and-stop service
High-temperature trailer towing
Sustained high-speed, high-temperature driving

and on supercharged diesel engines operating on high sulfur fuel.

DEFINITIONS AND EXPLANATION OF API ENGINE SERVICE CLASSIFICATIONS

The latest revised API Engine Service Classification System presently includes nine classes of service—five for service stations and four for commercial classifications. It is an "open-ended" system which permits the addition of new categories as required without changing or deleting existing categories.

The API letter designations identifying the nine service classifications, with reference to the previous API system and to related military and industry designations, are summarized in the following chart.

New API Engine Service Classifications	Previous API Engine Service Classifications	Related Designations Military and Industry
Service Station Engine Services		
SA	ML	Straight mineral oil
SB	MM	Inhibited oil
SC	MS (1964)	1964 MS Warranty Approved, M2C101A
SD	MS (1968)	1968 MS Warranty Approved, M2C101B3 6041-M (Prior to July 1970)
SE	None	1972 Warranty Approved, M2C101C3 6041-M (July 1970)
Commercial and Fleet Engine Services		
CA	DG	MIL-L-2104A
CB	DM	Supp. 1
CC	DM	MIL-L-2104B
CD	DS	MIL-L-45199B, Series 3

The following descriptions of API Engine Service Classifications are intended as guides to aid in the selection of the proper engine oils for significantly different engine conditions.

"S"—SERVICE (Service Stations, Garages, etc.)

SA for Utility Gasoline and Diesel Engine Service

Service typical of engines operated under such mild conditions that the protection afforded by compounded oils is not required. This classification has no performance requirements.

SB for Minimum Duty Gasoline Engine Service

Service typical of gasoline engines operated under such mild conditions that only minimum protection afforded by compounding is desired. Oils designed for this service have been used since the 1930's and provide only antiscuff capability and resistance to oil oxidation and bearing corrosion.

SC for 1964 Gasoline Engine Warranty Maintenance Service

Service typical of gasoline engines in 1964 through 1967 models of passenger cars and some trucks operating under engine manufacturers' warranties in effect during those models' years. Oils designed for this service provide control of high- and low-temperature deposits, wear, rust and corrosion in gasoline engines.

SD for 1968 Gasoline Engine Warranty Maintenance Service

Service typical of gasoline engines in 1968 through 1970 models of passenger cars and some trucks operating under engine manufacturers' warranties in effect during those models' years. Also may apply to certain 1971 and/or later models as specified (or recommended) in the owners' manuals. Oils designed for this service provide more protection against high- and low-temperature engine deposits, wear, rust and corrosion in gasoline engines than oils which are satisfactory for API Engine Service Classification SC and may be used when API Engine Service Classification SC is recommended.

SE for 1972 Gasoline Engine Warranty Maintenance Service

Service typical of gasoline engines in passenger cars and some trucks, beginning with 1972 and certain 1971 models, operating under engine manufacturers' warranties. Oils designed for this service provide more protection against oil oxidation, high-temperature engine deposits and rust and corrosion in gasoline engines than oils which are satisfactory for API Engine Service Classification SD or SC and may be used when either of these classifications is recommended.

A service station oil suitable for servicing new cars under warranty would be referred to as "API Service SE." If oils are suitable for more than one service, it is appropriate that these oils be so designated. For example, "API Service CC and SE."

"C"—COMMERCIAL (Fleets, Contractors, Farmers, etc.)

CA for Light Duty Diesel Engine Service

Service typical of diesel engines operated in mild to moderate duty with high quality fuels but occasionally has included gasoline engines in mild service. Oils designed for this service provide protection from bearing corrosion and from high-temperature deposits in normally aspirated diesel engines when using fuel of such quality that they impose no unusual requirements for wear and deposit protection. They were widely used in the late 1940's and 1950's.

CB for Moderate Duty Diesel Engine Service

Service typical of diesel engines operated in mild to moderate duty, but with lower quality fuels which necessitate more protection from wear and deposits. Occasionally has included gasoline engines in mild service. Oils designed for this service provide necessary protection from bearing corrosion and from high-temperature deposits in normally aspirated diesel engines with higher sulfur fuels. Oils designed for this service were introduced in 1949.

CC for Moderate Duty Diesel and Gasoline Engine Service

Service typical of lightly supercharged diesel engines—operated in moderate to severe duty—and certain heavy-duty gasoline engines. Oils designed for this service provide protection from high temperature deposits in lightly supercharged diesels and also from rust, corrosion and low temperature deposits in gasoline engines. These oils were introduced in 1961 and used in many trucks and in industrial and construction equipment and farm tractors.

CD for Severe Duty Diesel Engine Service

Service typical of supercharged diesel engines in high-speed, high-output duty requiring highly effective control of wear and deposits. Oils designed for this service were introduced in 1955 and provide protection from bearing corrosion and from high temperature deposits in supercharged diesel engines when using fuels of a wide quality range.

Oil Contamination

Under normal tractor operation the crankcase oil becomes contaminated with materials that get into the engine from the outside (external contaminants) or get into the oil from other parts of the engine or are formed in the engine (internal contaminants).

External Contaminants

Dirt and dust are breathed in with the combustion air in spite of the air cleaner.

Dirt and dust enter the crankcase through the crankcase breather in spite of the small air cleaner at the breather outlet.

Internal Contaminants

Unburned fuel is carried down past the rings during cold weather operation and during the warm up period. This dilutes the crankcase oil.

Water vapor, a product of combustion, tends to condense

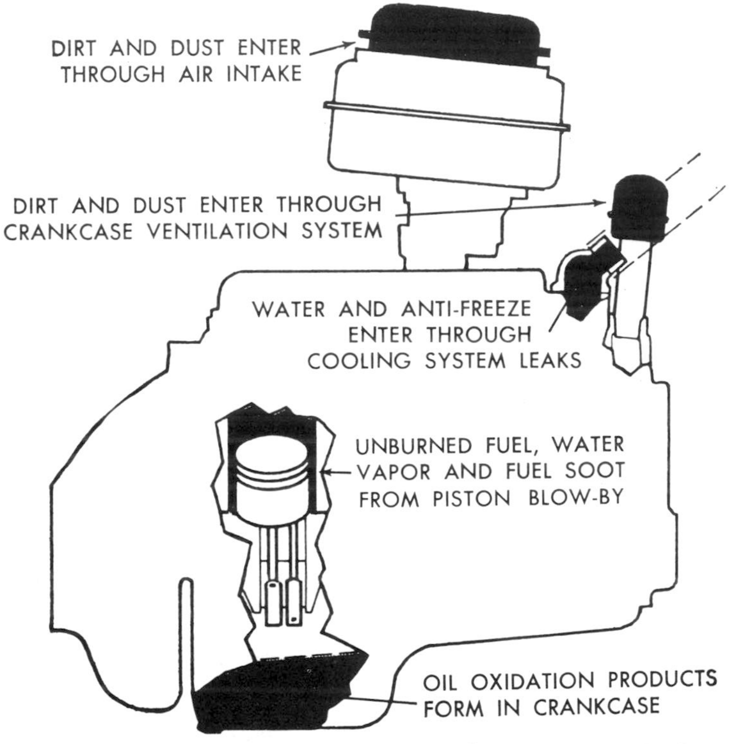

Courtesy American Oil Co.

Fig. 3-14–How various contaminants get into automobile or truck engine. The same contaminants get into a tractor engine. Draining the crankcase regularly will remove them.

and collect in the crankcase during cold weather operation. Water causes rusting, especially during periods when the tractor is not used frequently. Water also combines with other contaminants to form cold-engine sludge, a grey, pasty-like material which can plug oil filters, rings and oil lines.

Fuel soot accumulates as a result of incomplete burning of the fuel.

Cooling water can leak into the crankcase. If anti-freeze gets into the crankcase, deposits may form which will cause engine seizure.

Oil oxidation will take place as a result of high temperature operation and, if allowed to accumulate, may cause varnish and other hot-engine sludge formations.

Oil Change Recommendations

The primary purpose of draining the oil in an engine is to remove the contaminants that have accumulated in that oil. The additives in a modern oil can perform their functions until the recommended oil change period, but if the oil is kept in the engine beyond this period they tend to lose their effectiveness and engine deposits may form.

The engine manufacturer's recommendation should be followed in changing oil and in changing filters. If the tractor is used for chore-work, change oil more frequently. In extremely dusty

Courtesy American Oil Co.

Fig. 3-15—Plugged oil filter due to low temperature operation and improper servicing.

conditions, change more frequently. The most important single factor in keeping the engine clean is to drain the oil when the engine is hot.

The oil change interval recommended by most tractor manufacturers varies from 75 to not over 100 hours under good conditions. When the tractor is operated under unusual conditions, such as excessive heat, cold, dust, frequent starts and stops, or with poor quality fuels or lubricants, the oil should be changed at more frequent intervals.

STORING AND HANDLING LUBRICATING OILS

Lubricating oil is clean when delivered. It is usually in drums or sealed cans. There are several precautions to observe in keeping oil clean and uncontaminated until it can be placed in the engine.

Inside storage—

1. Store drums and cans in a dust free location.
2. Keep pumps, filler cans, measures and funnels free from dust.
3. Wipe off top of drum before changing pump.

Outside storage—

1. Store drums under shelter.
2. Tighten bungs with a wrench and wooden hammer.
3. If cover can not be provided, store drums on their sides on a rock.
4. If drums must be stored upright, tilt them so that water will collect away from bungs.

General suggestions—

1. Wipe off around filler pipe of engine before putting in new oil.
2. Wipe off end of can before opening canned oil.
3. Keep funnels, filler cans and filler spouts clean.
4. Wipe up spilled oil.

GREASE

Lubricating grease is ordinarily a blend of lubricating oil and soap with stabilizers and additives. The kind of soap used determines the special properties of the grease. Calcium, sodium and lithium soaps are most commonly used.

Calcium soap—pressure gun or chassis grease.

Sodium soap—wheel bearing grease.

Lithium soap—multi-purpose grease.

The development of multi-purpose grease has made it possible for the tractor operator to use one grease for all grease fittings and hand packed bearings.

Many operator's manuals recommend wheel bearing grease for packing wheel bearings, but multi-purpose grease is now considered to be satisfactory for wheel bearing lubrication. It is recommended that wheel bearings be packed only one half to two-thirds full with multi-purpose grease.

Multi-purpose grease is water resistant, will withstand high temperature, protects against rust and is long lasting.

General suggestions—

1. Keep the grease containers in a dust free place.
2. Wipe off the grease gun before filling it.
3. A method of filling the grease gun without exposing the grease to dust and dirt is recommended. There are several devices on the market.
4. Always wipe off grease fittings before applying grease. Don't force dirt into a bearing. Wipe off excess grease after greasing.
5. Grease the tractor at the end of the day when it is warm.

QUESTIONS

1. What are the three fuels commonly used in modern tractors?
2. What is the meaning of compression ratio?
3. Why is a high compression engine more efficient?
4. What is the meaning of octane number?

5. What is detonation or "knocking"?
6. What causes detonation?
7. What is the meaning of cetane number of diesel fuel?
8. Do octane number and cetane number indicate similar qualities in fuel?
9. What is the difference between summer grade and winter grade gasoline?
10. What is the difference between Grade 1-D and 2-D diesel fuel?
11. Why is storing a large quantity of fuel a poor practice?
12. Why is gasoline difficult to store?
13. Explain the operation of a pressure cap on a gasoline storage tank.
14. What are the major safety precautions in storing and handling gasoline?
15. What precautions should be followed in storing LP Gas?
16. What important suggestions should be followed in storing diesel fuel?
17. What are the uses of lubricating oil in the engine crankcase?
18. What are the additives in a modern lubricating oil?
19. What is the difference between 10W and 10W-30 oil?
20. What is the difference between a Service SD and a Service SE oil?
21. What contaminants accumulate in crankcase oil?
22. What suggestions should be followed in handling grease?
23. What is the difference between wheel bearing grease and a multi-purpose grease?

Part II

PREVENTIVE MAINTENANCE

Courtesy Allis-Chalmers Corp.

With careful maintenance, this tractor with a 426 cu. in. displacement will give many hours of service.

CHAPTER 4

THE MEANING OF PREVENTIVE MAINTENANCE

INTRODUCTION

The modern farm tractor is the result of many years of development. Its present efficiency is possible because of engineering progress in design, metallurgy, fuels, lubricants and manufacturing methods. The modern tractor engine is very closely

Courtesy Deere & Company Service Publications

Fig. 4-1—The modern tractor works long hours in clouds of dirt and dust. It is fitted with accessories designed to keep grit away from vital working parts. Do your part by keeping the accessories working efficiently.

related to the modern truck, automobile, small airplane, speed boat and diesel-powered locomotive. All have one feature in common; the internal combustion engine. The engine used may be two or four stroke cycle; single or multiple cylinder; manifold or solid fuel injection; low, medium or high compression; a gasoline or fuel-oil burner; but it is still an internal combustion engine. All internal combustion engines have many things in common. They all require constant, systematic, intelligent care and maintenance to insure greatest efficiency, freedom from trouble and long life. Maintaining peak efficiency in the modern tractor is largely a matter of following fairly well-defined maintenance practices.

The farm tractor is a hard-working piece of precision machinery. It is capable of working long hours at capacity loads in the heat and dust of summer or in the cold and snow of winter.

Courtesy International Harvester Co.

Fig. 4-2—A modern tractor must operate efficiently in the heat of summer as well as in the cold of winter.

The finest and most appropriate materials go into its construction. Highly skilled workmen use highly specialized and intricate tools in its manufacture. Fine adjustments are made to insure satisfactory operation over a long period of time.

The manufacturer guarantees good materials and good workmanship. Continued good performance over a long period of time, however, is strictly up to the operator. A careless operator can allow a tractor engine to ruin itself in a few minutes or a few hours. A careful operator can greatly prolong the useful life and efficiency of a similar engine.

The author knows of many, many instances where tractor engines have had to be overhauled because simple maintenance and servicing was not done.

Example 1. The hose connection between the carburetor and air cleaner was removed to relieve a flooded carburetor. The tractor

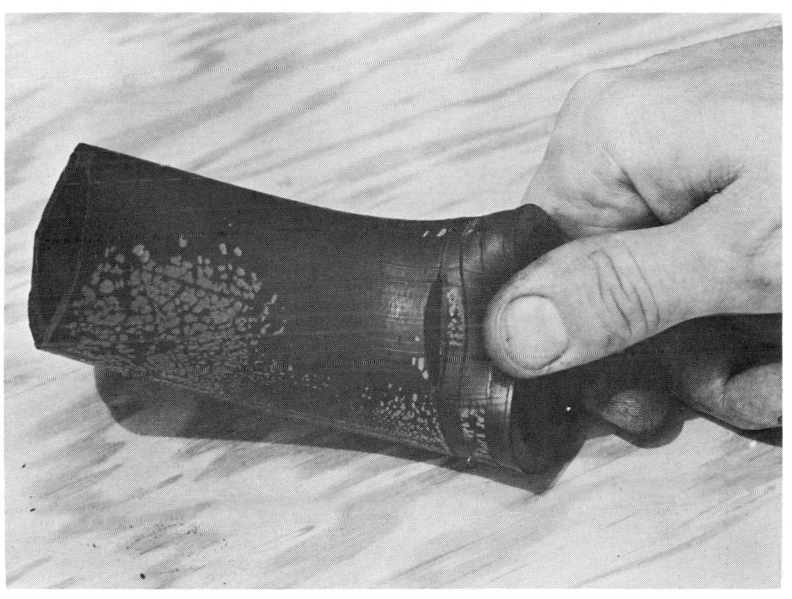

Courtesy American Oil Co.

Fig. 4-3—Cracked air cleaner hose connection.

was started and operated one half day before the loose connection was noticed. A complete overhaul, which included bearings, valves, valve guides, sleeves, rings and pistons, was necessary.
Example 2. The upper hose connection between the carburetor and air cleaner on this tractor deteriorated and cracked. The tractor was pulling a combine in soybeans. There was a gradual loss of power and when the tractor was taken into the shop for repair a new engine had to be installed.

Courtesy American Oil Co.

Fig. 4-4—Air cleaner pipe with hole worn in it.

Example 3. An engine had to be replaced in a new tractor because of high oil consumption. The cylinder walls were scored. A factory representative was sent out when there was a complaint of loss of power on the replacement engine. He found the operator pulling a wagon, loading baled hay with the tractor idling at less than half the slow idle speed recommended. The operator thought there was adequate lubrication because the oil pressure gauge showed pressure.

It is with the hope of preventing similar costly, unnecessary repairs that this book has been written.

PREVENTIVE MAINTENANCE

By preventive maintenance we mean–

Servicing,

Adjusting,

Operating,

Repairing, and

Caring for a tractor so that–

Unnecessary wear is prevented,

Time lost due to breakdowns is held to a minimum,

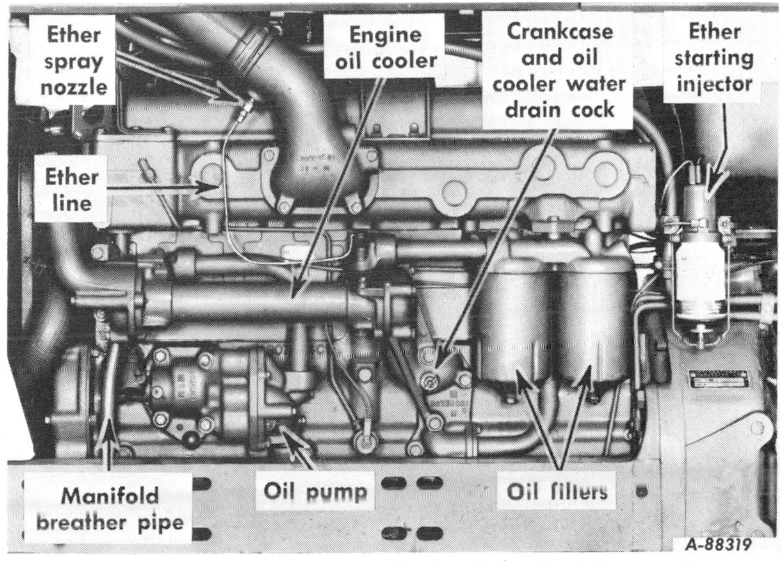

Courtesy International Harvester Co.

Fig. 4-5–Side view of a diesel tractor. Note the oil filters, manifold breather pipe and ether starting injector. Information on servicing these parts is in the Operator's Manual. Read it carefully.

Satisfactory performance is the rule rather than the exception,
The useful life built in by the manufacturer is profitably
realized by the operator.

The key man in preventive maintenance is the tractor operator. There is a great deal of difference between an operator and a person who merely drives the tractor.

The careful operator is familiar with the tractor. He has studied the operator's manual, he understands how to correctly operate the controls and watches the oil pressure and temperature gauges and charge indicator. He sees that the tractor is regularly

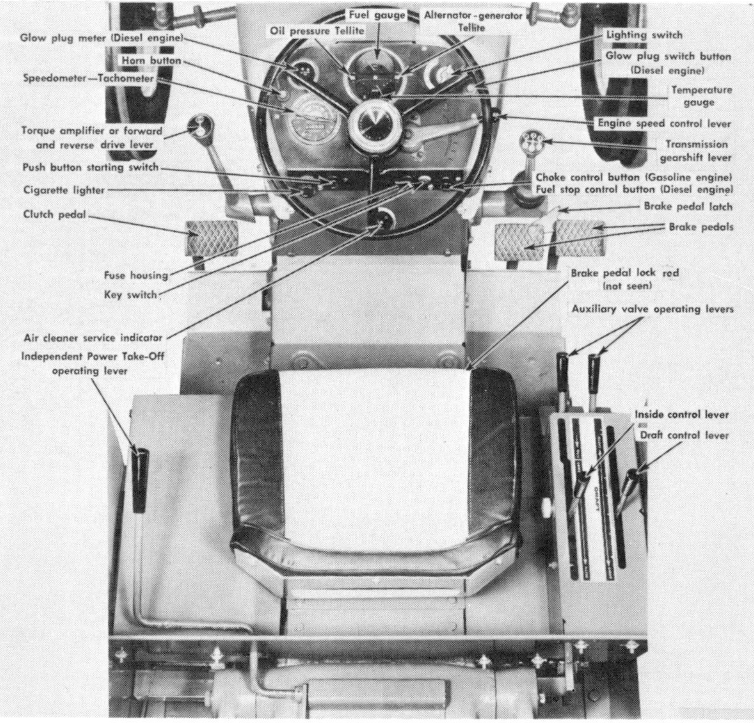

Courtesy International Harvester Co.

Fig. 4-6—Instrument panel and controls.

Courtesy John Deere, Moline, Ill.

Fig. 4-7–The tractor will respond to frequent lubrication.

Courtesy Purdue University Cooperative Extension Service

Fig. 4-8–Plugged air cleaner from a tractor that had been taken to a dealer for overhaul because of loss of power. This air cleaner had not been serviced for a long time. Note the plugged screen.

Courtesy John Deere, Moline, Ill.

Fig. 4-9—Clashing gears cause unnecessary wear.

Courtesy American Oil Co.

Fig. 4-10—Tractor gears are strong and sturdy but a worn bearing will soon allow them to cut out due to misalignment.

serviced with the right fuel, oil, grease and coolant. He is alert for any odd sound or action in the tractor that might indicate faulty functioning of any part. He operates the tractor at the correct speed in the right gear for the job. He protects the tractor when it is stored for a period of time.

The careful operator needs correct information, experience and desire to succeed with preventive maintenance. The best

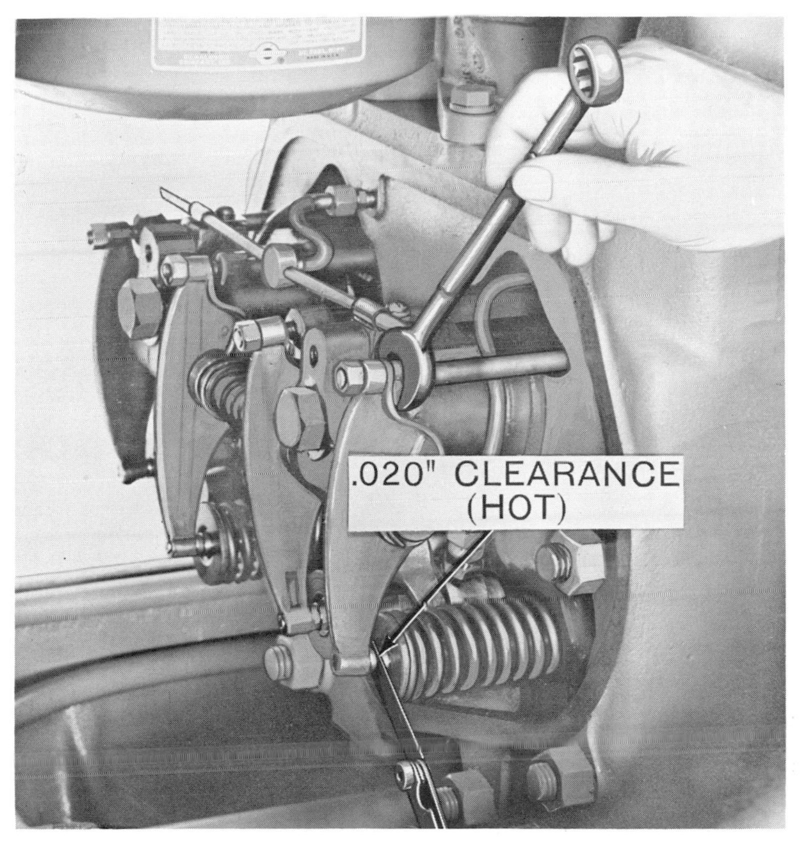

Courtesy John Deere, Moline, Ill.

Fig. 4-11–Adjusting valve tappet clearance.

source of information is the operator's manual supplied by the manufacturer, plus the advice of the service manager at the local dealer's. Experience is gained by operating and maintaining the tractor. A mistake in maintenance resulting in a costly repair is costly experience but is not at all uncommon. The desire to practice preventive maintenance usually comes as a result of knowledge and experience.

The Operator's Responsibility

The operator has a lot to do with the way his engine performs. He should be able to:

Choose and use the proper fuel for his engine.

Adjust the carburetor to get the correct mixture.

Determine when repair work is necessary to restore correct compression, such as grinding valves; replacing the head gasket; installing new pistons, or rings or both, or replacing the cylinder assembly.

Adjust valves.

Time ignition.

Detect and correct ignition troubles or direct the work to be done.

Courtesy John Deere, Moline, Ill.

Fig. 4-12–Do not overload the tractor.

Choose the correct lubricant, change it when necessary, and add to it as needed.

Prevent or correct cooling troubles.

Keep engine serviced properly at all times.

Refrain from overloading.

If the operator will but do his part, the tractor, with the excellent design, fine materials, and expert workmanship that the manufacturer has put into it, will have a chance to work for many years as it was intended to do, and without major troubles.

Some operators will do major overhaul work on their tractors such as replacing sleeves and pistons, grinding valves and replacing piston rings. It is usually best, however, for the op-

Courtesy American Oil Co.

Fig. 4-13—Detonation has caused this piston to burn at the edge.

erator to concentrate on preventive maintenance for the purpose of preventing unnecessary overhaul due to neglect and lack of servicing.

When an overhaul becomes necessary, the work should be done by a qualified mechanic with lots of experience and the necessary tools and equipment.

QUESTIONS

1. What is the meaning of preventive maintenance?
2. What does preventive maintenance prevent?
3. Who is the key man in practicing preventive maintenance—the manufacturer, the dealer or the operator?
4. Where can the operator secure information on preventive maintenance?
5. Who usually does major overhaul on a tractor—the operator or a mechanic?
6. Why does idling a tractor too slowly result in damage to cylinders and rings?
7. Why is an air-tight connection between the air cleaner and carburetor so important?

CHAPTER 5

THE STEPS IN GENERAL MAINTENANCE

Successful preventive maintenance starts with the run-in of a new tractor. Each daily and periodic lubrication, service and adjustment job is then a step in the maintenance of that tractor.

STEPS

Step 1. Run-in of the new tractor.
Step 2. Daily warm up of the tractor.
Step 3. Daily or 10 hour service jobs.
Step 4. Weekly or 50 hour service jobs.
Step 5. 100 hour service jobs.
Step 6. 200 to 300 hour service jobs.
Step 7. 500 hour or every six month service jobs.
Step 8. 1000 hour or yearly service jobs.

Courtesy John Deere, Moline, Ill.

Fig. 5-1—Nothing like a yearly check-up.

1. Run-in Period.

The most critical period in the service life of a new or overhauled tractor engine is the first 50 to 100 hours of operation. This period is known as the run-in or "break-in" period, and it is essential to follow the recommendations in the Operator's Manual during this period.

The way the tractor is operated during the first 100 hours will influence the power the engine develops and can prolong the service life of the engine. The engine must not be idled excessively during this period and must not be put under a full-rated load. The tractor should be operated at reduced loads but at the normal throttle setting. The load on the tractor can be reduced by shifting down one or two gears from that normally used.

Courtesy American Oil Co.

Fig. 5-2—This aluminum piston taken from a new tractor broken in by doing light work in cold weather shows how moisture has caused pitting of the piston. The cross head fin bushing was also corroded and stuck. This could have been prevented if the tractor had been thoroughly warmed up each time it was started.

If the tractor is lugged down below its rated engine RPM during the run-in period, damage to the piston rings and cylinder walls is almost sure to occur. The piston rings have to seat in with the cylinder walls to make a good seal. A heavy load on the tractor before the rings are seated will permit blow-by of high-temperature gases from the combustion chamber. These hot gases tend to collapse the upper piston rings and cause them to carbon up and stick to such an extent that they will never seat to the cylinder walls. The result will be loss of power, excessive oil consumption and extremely short engine life.

The author knows of one instance where a new tractor was purchased on Thursday and pulled in a tractor pulling contest on Saturday. The tractor was in the shop the following week for a ring and valve job.

The brakes, bearings and gears will also benefit from a careful run-in period.

During the run-in period the head bolts should be torqued and the valve clearance should be checked and adjusted as recommended in the Operator's Manual. Hub clamp bolts, manifold bolts and all external bolts and cap screws should be tightened. Fan belts will stretch and probably will need to be tightened. Check the hose connections between the air cleaner and carburetor or manifold to make sure no dirty air can be drawn into the system and bypass the air cleaner.

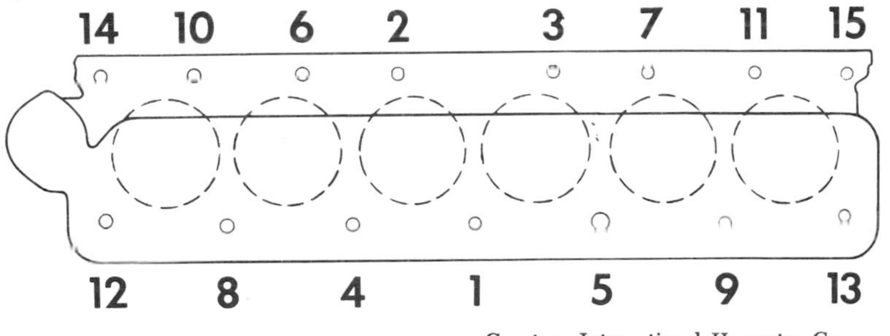

Courtesy International Harvester Co.

Fig. 5-3—Tightening sequence for cylinder head bolts on a gasoline or LP gas engine.

Change the engine oil, engine oil filter and transmission-hydraulic system filter at some time during the first 100 hours as specified by the manufacturer.

Foreign material and some metal from the wearing-in of the engine accumulate in the engine oil and transmission-hydraulic system during the run-in period. It is imperative that the initial engine oil and engine oil filter change be made at the end of the period specified in the Operator's Manual to remove this accumulation. The hydraulic system filter must be changed at the specified time because the filter will have trapped any foreign material being circulated in the transmission-hydraulic system.

The recommendations for the initial oil and filter change vary with manufacturers. Some recommend the change at the end of 20 hours, some at 50 hours and others at the end of 100 hours. These recommendations are based on the design of the engine and the manufacturers' experience with each tractor. Some tractors are delivered with 10W break-in oil in the crankcase. It is extremely important that the break-in oil be used for the specified number of hours and then be replaced with the correct weight and quality of oil for the anticipated air temperature during the next oil change period. Obviously, the engine should not be placed under the full-rated load with a lightweight oil in the crankcase.

Making the initial oil and filter change as recommended helps insure a long service life for the tractor and keeps the engine warranty in effect.

2. Warm-up Period.

The useful service life of any tractor will be lengthened, if the operator will make a practice of always permitting the engine to warm-up before putting the tractor under full load. This is particularly important if the tractor is going to be operated where there is a lot of moisture in the air such as in and out of a dairy barn in cold weather.

For field work, even in the summer, it is a good practice to idle the engine at about half speed for 5 minutes and at full throttle for the same length of time before putting it under full

Courtesy International Harvester Co.

Fig. 5-4—Don't place the tractor under a heavy load until the temperature gauge is up to normal operating temperature.

load. Operating in a lower gear for the first 30 minutes after getting into the field is another good practice. Warming the tractor thoroughly guarantees good lubrication of all engine parts and cuts down on the moisture that will condense in the crankcase when the engine is cold. This moisture tends to form sludge and other engine deposits.

NOTE: Prolonged idling tends to cool the engine rather than warm it.

Hitching to an implement and driving to the field automatically takes care of the warm-up in most instances. That is the reason we usually get good service life from the tractor.

Excessive wear will occur when the tractor is parked in the field, is started and placed under a full load immediately. In a situation of this kind a lower gear than normal should be used for the first half hour.

Practically all engine wear occurs in the interval after starting the engine and before the engine reaches operating temperature. The operating temperature of most tractor engines is between 180 and 190 degrees. It takes at least 30 minutes of operation for the engine to reach this temperature.

Stopping the Engine

ALWAYS allow the engine to cool slowly after full-load operation by idling the engine for a short time. The cooling-off period is as important as the warm-up period but for different reasons. When the engine is stopped while hot the valves that are closed cool so rapidly they may check or crack. This damage shortens valve life radically.

When an automobile is driven up to the gasoline pumps at a service station, the attendant usually asks to check the water and oil and while doing this usually checks the level of the battery "water." These service jobs or maintenance checks are essentially what should be done as daily or 10 hour service jobs on a tractor.

3. Daily or 10 Hour Service Jobs.

There are many preventive maintenance jobs that are routine and performed daily. Examples are: checking the crankcase oil level, checking the water or antifreeze level in the radiator, check-

Courtesy John Deere, Moline, Ill.

Fig. 5-5—The tractor will respond to frequent lubrication.

ing the air cleaner and lubricating with a pressure gun the fittings requiring daily lubrication. These fittings are usually on parts

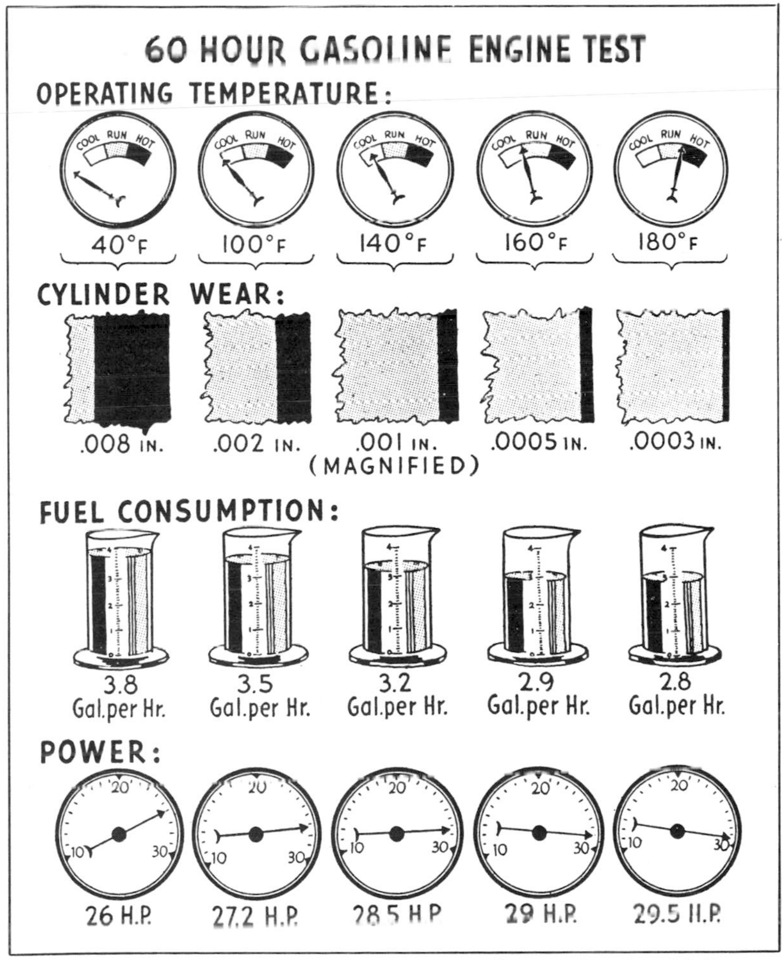

Courtesy American Oil Co.

Fig. 5-6—This illustration shows the importance of maintaining high engine temperature. Note that as operating temperature increases up to 180°F., cylinder wear decreases, fuel consumption decreases, and power increases.

exposed to dust and dirt and are lubricated daily to force out old grease and dirt.

These daily jobs are critical, because failure to perform them can lead to serious damage to the tractor. A neglected air cleaner can cause the engine to be ruined in less than a day as can low crankcase oil level or low coolant level in the radiator.

Making sure that these items are taken care of is one of the most important steps in preventive maintenance.

4. Weekly or 50 Hour Service Jobs.

On some tractors there are lubrication points that need attention once a week or after 50 hours of operation. Examples are water pump bearings, fan shaft bearings, power take-off clutch bearings and drawbar rollers. It is wise to check battery fluid level and tire pressure once a week.

5. 100 Hour Service Jobs.

The recommended engine oil change period has been reduced to 100 hours on practically all tractor engines. One manufacturer recommends the oil change at 75 hours. The usual recommendation for the engine oil filter change is at every other oil change.

6. 200 to 300 Hour Service Jobs.

On some tractors there are lubrication points that should be serviced approximately every month or at the end of 200 hours. There will usually be only a few points to lubricate but there are other checks and adjustments to be made at this time. On some tractors the hydraulic oil filter in the steering and power brake system and power shift system should be changed at 250 hours. It is wise to check the tightness of front and rear wheel bolts about every 200 hours.

The transmission clutch pedal free travel should be checked. There should usually be 1½ to 1¾ inches of free pedal travel. Lack of clearance will cause overheating of the clutch due to slippage, loss of power and early replacement of the clutch facing.

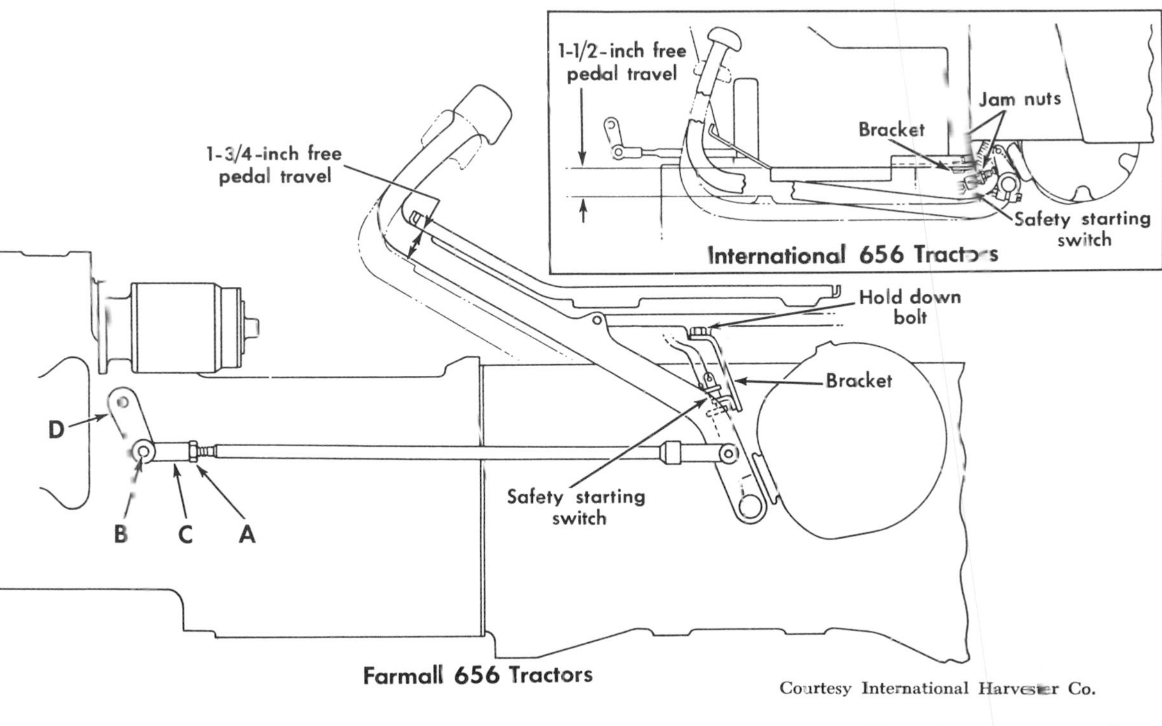

Courtesy International Harvester Co.

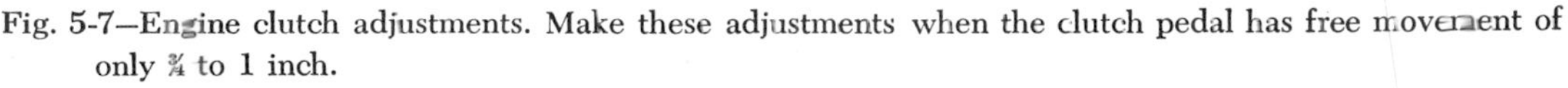

Fig. 5-7—Engine clutch adjustments. Make these adjustments when the clutch pedal has free movement of only ¾ to 1 inch.

The brakes should be checked for free movement and equal pressure and adjusted if necessary. Power brakes on some makes of tractor are adjusted by bleeding air from the power brake system according to the instructions in the Operator's Manual.

There is a tendency to overlook the lubrication points that are lubricated only at long intervals. It is a good idea to check the Operator's Manual occasionally to make sure no parts are being missed in the regular lubrication of the tractor.

Courtesy International Harvester Co.

Fig. 5-8—This instrument records engine hours of operation, shows normal tractor speeds in miles per hour, and indicates the correct engine speed for power take-off operations.

7. 500 Hour or Every Six Month Service Jobs.

About every six months or after 500 hours of operation, there are several important service jobs that need to be done. Examples are: clean and repack the front wheel bearings, change the hydraulic system oil, check the oil level in the steering gear housing and perform the other service jobs and adjustments recommended in the Operator's Manual for the tractor being serviced. These jobs logically should be done in the spring and in the fall.

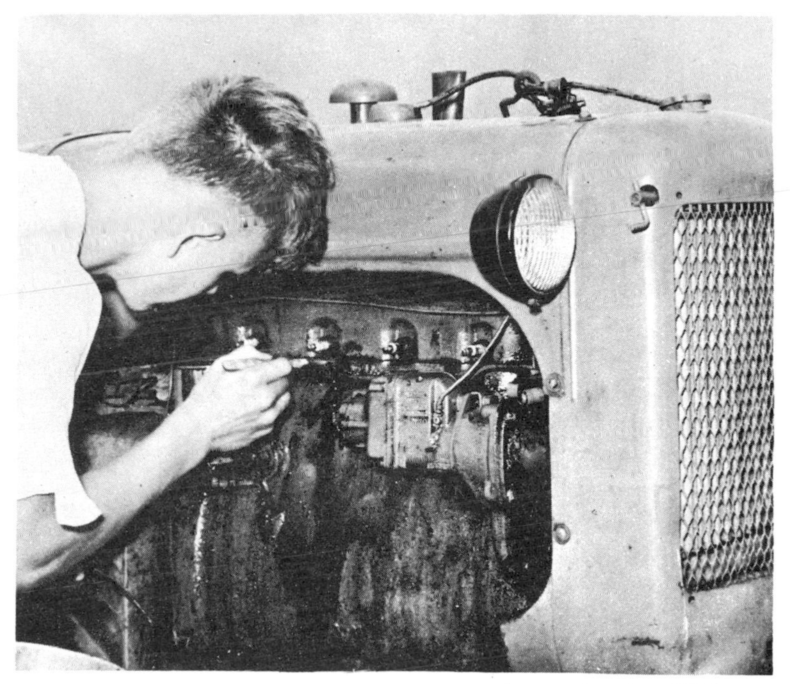

Courtesy American Oil Co.

Fig. 5-9—Use a safe commercial solvent or kerosene when cleaning the engine and other tractor parts. Don't ever use gasoline.

8. 1000 Hour or Yearly Service Jobs.

Once a year or after 1000 hours of operation, there are more service jobs that need to be done. Examples are: drain and refill transmission, differential and final drives, lubricate the rear axle on some makes of tractors, lubricate the fan bearing. The Operator's Manual will designate the service jobs that should be done once a year and this will vary with makes.

Once a year the tractor should be gone over thoroughly and tuned-up. This should be done during the winter in preparation for the busy season. It can be done by the dealer service department or by an experienced operator. In the tune-up of the tractor, the following jobs should be done:

1. Drain, flush and check radiator and cooling system.
2. Check ignition system—points, plugs and timing.
3. Check electrical system – generator, starter, wiring and switches.
4. Check the fuel system—carburetor, sediment bowl and tank. A diesel engine will have several important jobs to be done on the fuel filters and injection system.
5. Check the air cleaner—bowl, pipes and hose connections.
6. Check the crankcase breather.
7. Check the engine compression.
8. Check and adjust the valves.
9. Check the hydraulic system—drain, flush and refill if necessary.
10. Drain, flush and refill the transmission, differential and final drives.
11. Clean and repack front wheel bearings.
12. Inspect and adjust the brakes.
13. Inspect and adjust the steering mechanism.
14. Check and tighten all nuts and cap screws.

Systematically following a maintenance procedure similar to this will add years to the life of the tractor and prevent unnecessary break downs.

QUESTIONS

1. Why is the run-in period critical in the life of the tractor?
2. What damage may occur if the tractor is not run-in correctly?
3. How can a new tractor be operated at less than full load during the first week of operation?
4. What damage may occur when a tractor is idled excessively?
5. Which is more likely to cause damage, running a new tractor at full throttle or allowing it to idle excessively?
6. Most of the wear occurs during what period in the operation of the tractor?

CHAPTER 6

MAINTAINING THE LUBRICATION SYSTEM

Lubrication probably is the greatest single factor contributing to the life of the tractor and to its satisfactory operation. Two different types of lubricants are used in the tractor-oils and greases. In general, oil is used in the crankcase of the engine and in the gear cases, while greases are used to lubricate all other moving parts.

The lubricating oil is circulated constantly throughout the engine. It is exposed to temperatures ranging from 140° to 250° and must not break down under these changes in temperature. It is expected to reduce friction, prevent wear, transfer heat, seal compression, and keep the inside of the engine clean. In order for the lubricating oil to perform these duties, the system must be

Courtesy International Harvester Co.

Fig. 6-1—Stop the engine if the oil pressure gauge does not show oil pressure. Pressure does not guarantee, however, that oil is circulating if the engine is idling too slowly.

kept free from sludge, the oil passage-ways must not become plugged, the filter must clean the oil, and the oil pump must circulate the oil.

Engines are ordinarily lubricated by one of three systems.

1. Splash

The splash system is common on single-cylinder engines. Oil

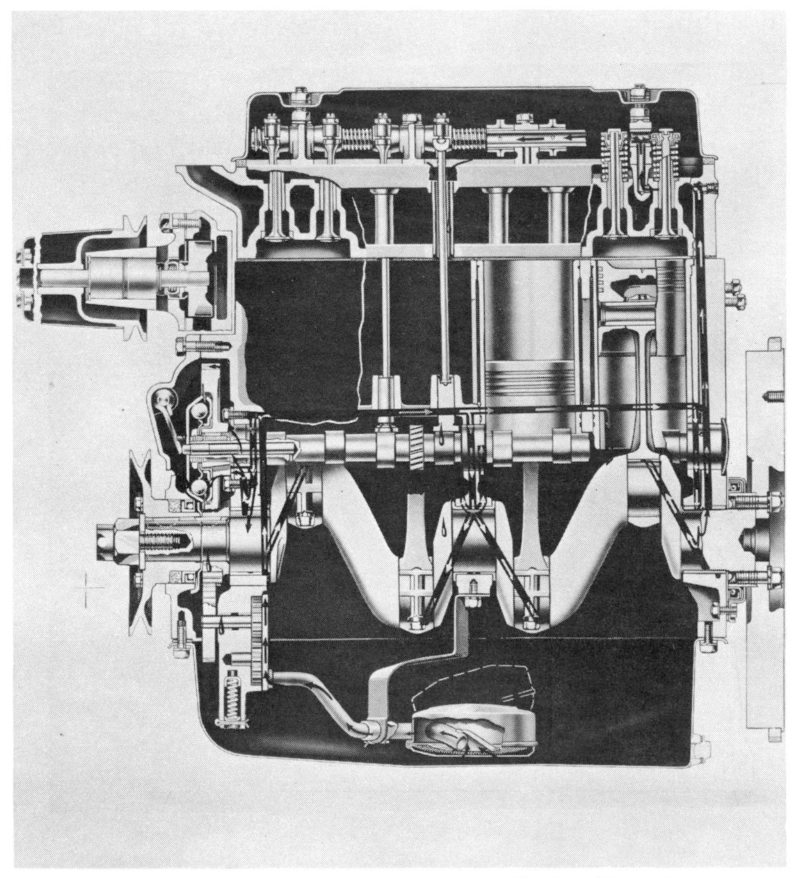

Courtesy Massey-Ferguson

Fig. 6-2–Side view of an engine with a force-feed lubrication system. Follow the path of the oil to all parts of the engine.

is contained in the crankcase and is splashed throughout the engine by the connecting rod, governor weights or other moving parts.

2. Circulating Splash

There is an oil pump in this system. It may be found on some of the smaller tractor engines. The oil is pumped to dip troughs where projections on the connecting rods pick it up and throw it to other moving parts. This is satisfactory for light duty engines, if the proper oil level is maintained.

3. Force-Feed

This is the most common system in use today. The oil is picked up by the oil pump through a screened inlet tube and pumped to

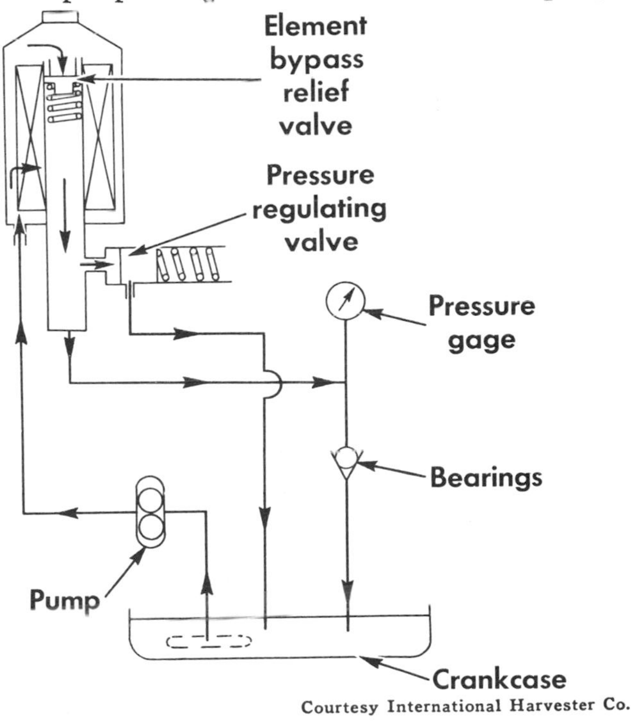

Fig. 6-3—Diagram of full flow oil filtering system.

the main bearings. The crankshaft is drilled to the crank throws so that oil is forced to the connecting rod bearings. The rods on some engines are drilled so that oil is carried under pressure directly to the wrist pins. Passages carry oil under pressure to the timing gears, camshaft bearings, rocker arms and tappets. The cylinders and pistons are lubricated by a spray from the ends of the connecting rod bearings.

The force-feed system with a full-flow filter is becoming common in modern tractor engines.

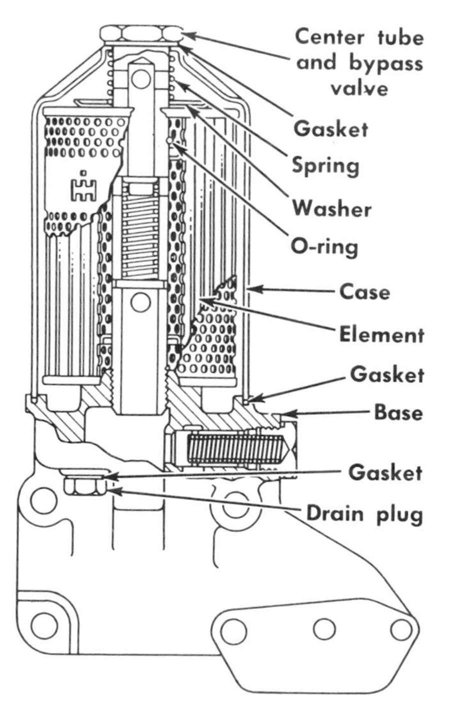

Courtesy International Harvester Co.

Fig. 6-4–Cutaway view of the oil filter.

The maintenance of the lubrication system consists of: Using good quality oil of the right viscosity,

Draining the oil regularly,
Changing the oil filter regularly,
Checking for and repairing leaks,
Keeping dust and dirt out of the system.

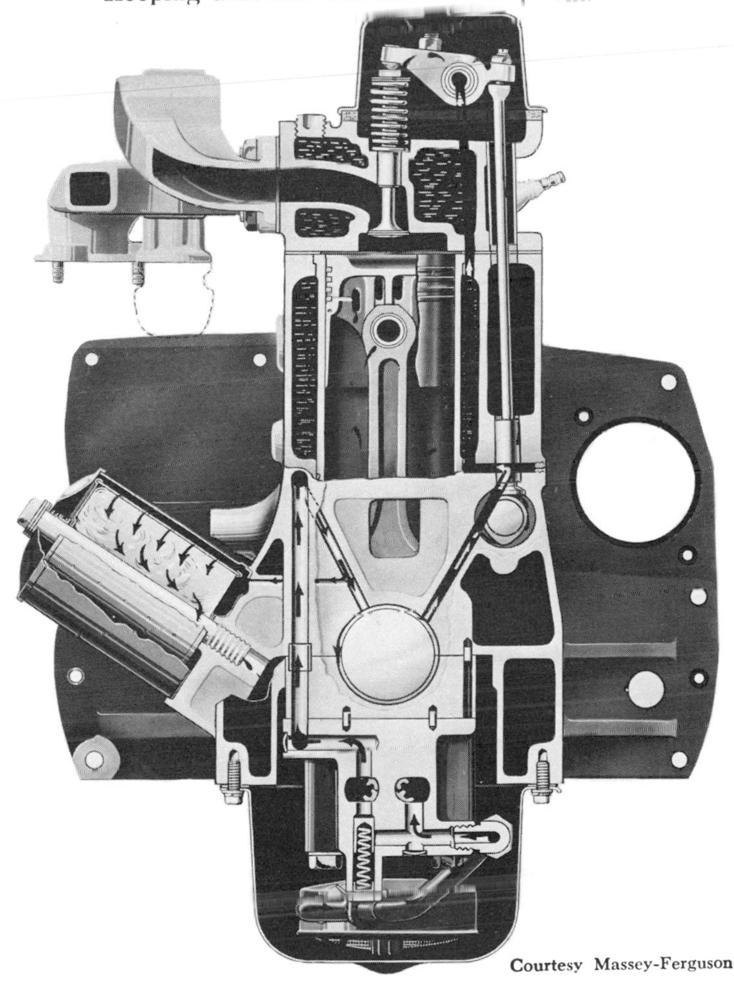

Courtesy Massey-Ferguson

Fig. 6-5—End view of an engine with a force-feed lubrication system. Note the path the oil takes to the oil filter and to the rocker arms. What happens if the oil filter becomes plugged?

The use of a top quality engine oil of the correct viscosity cannot be overemphasized. The Operator's Manual will specify the viscosity to use for the anticipated average temperature under which the tractor will be operating.

The quality of oil to use in the engine will be specified according to the API Engine Service Classifications. For gasoline engines this will usually be SD, CC or possibly CD, and for

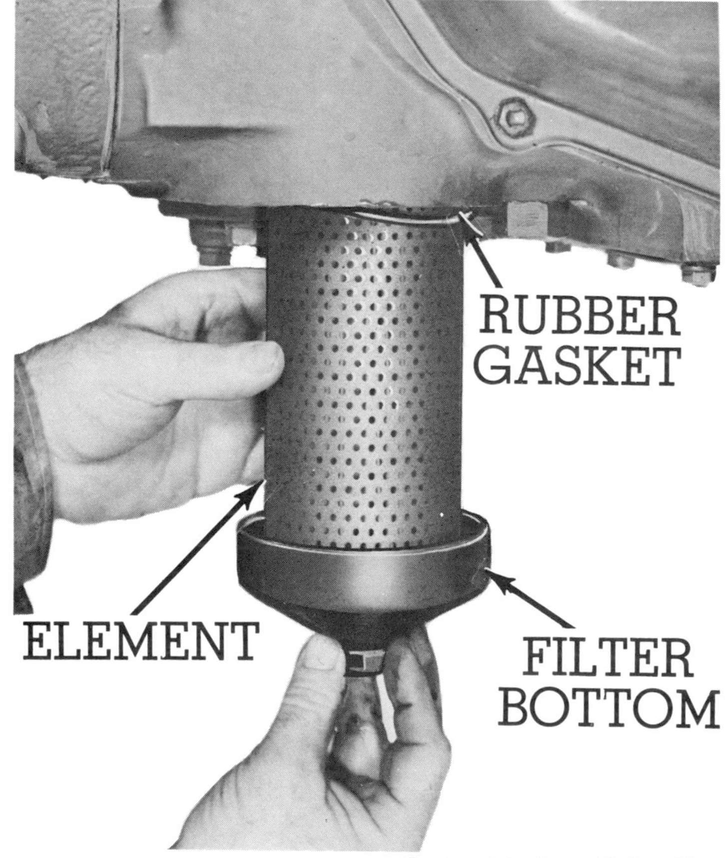

Courtesy John Deere, Moline, Ill.

Fig. 6-6—Oil filter elements. Be sure the gasket is in good condition and in place. Draw the filter cap up firmly, but do not over-tighten.

diesel engines it will be CD. Most manufacturers want the CD oil used to also meet the qualifications for a Series 3 oil.

A "Low Ash" engine oil should be used in an LP gas engine operated under heavy loads. The oil does not contain barium or calcium additive compounds blended into other oils to add rust preventive properties. An LP gas engine should not sit idle or be stored any great length of time with "Low Ash" oil in the crankcase. For storage, the crankcase should be filled with SD or CC oil to prevent rusting.

The next important step in maintaining the lubrication system is to drain the oil regularly. A good quality modern oil will normally darken with use. This does not indicate that the oil is getting dirty, it simply means that it is doing what it was designed to do—hold in suspension soot and carbon until it can be drained out of the engine. With this type of oil it is very important that the oil be drained while these by products of combustion are still being carried in the oil so that they can be removed *from* the engine rather than be deposited *in* the engine.

Procedure

1. Drain the crankcase oil.
   a. Drain when the engine is hot. (It does very little good to drain the oil from a cold engine.)
   b. Let the oil drain long enough to get it all out.
   c. Replace the oil drain plug.
2. Change the oil filter element.
   a. Remove the old filter element.
   b. Wipe out the filter case.
   c. Install a new filter. (Use the type recommended by the manufacturer.)
   d. Install new gaskets and seal rings.
   e. Replace the filter cap and tighten firmly, but not too tightly.
3. Fill the crankcase with new oil.
   a. Clean all dust and dirt from around the fill pipe.
   b. Use clean containers for the oil.
   c. Add enough oil to fill the filter—usually one quart.
   d. Replace the filler cap; in many cases this is the breather cap.

Courtesy John Deere, Moline, Ill.

Fig. 6-7—Replacing crankcase oil filter element.

4. Start the engine and run for several minutes.
5. Check for oil leaks.
   a. If there are leaks around the filter, tighten the cap slightly. If this doesn't stop the leak, the gasket may not be in place correctly.
6. Stop the engine and check the oil level.

It is a good practice to drop the oil pan about once a year to clean out accumulated sludge and to clean the oil pump inlet screen. This may be done when the regular tune-up is done.

Procedure

1. Remove the oil pan.
   a. Secure a new pan gasket.
   b. Remove the cap screws that hold the pan in place.
   c. Remove the pan and empty oil.
   d. Scrape the old gasket from the pan or crankcase.
   e. Wash the pan inside and out with kerosene or solvent.
2. Remove the oil pump inlet screen and wash thoroughly.
3. If it is desired, the inside of the engine can now be washed with clean solvent and a clean brush.
4. Examine the bearings for wear and check for any condition that needs attention.
5. Replace the oil pump screen.
6. Replace the oil pan.
   a. Install a new gasket.
   b. Replace the pan and tighten the cap screws.
7. Put fresh oil in the crankcase.
8. Run the engine and check for oil leaks.

Once a year or after 1000 hours of operation, the transmission, differential and final drives should be drained, flushed and refilled. If this is carefully done, it should prevent any break down in these parts during the life of the tractor. Any repair involving the transmission or differential is usually very costly and should be prevented, if at all possible.

Procedure

1. Drain the transmission, differential and final drive cases.
   a. Thoroughly warm-up the tractor.
   b. Remove all drain plugs and drain the cases while the tractor is warm.
2. Flush the transmission, differential and final drive cases.
   a. Replace drain plugs.
   b. Thoroughly clean around the filler openings.

c. Place the flushing oil in the cases. (Use the oil recommended by the tractor manufacturer. Kerosene is recommended by some.)
d. Jack up one rear wheel.
e. Place the tractor in low gear and run for a few minutes.
f. Completely drain all cases.
g. Replace the drain plugs.

3. Refill all cases with the right amount of the correct weight oil.
   a. Drive the tractor around for a while and check for leaks at the drain plugs.

In late model tractors the transmission-hydraulic system is lubricated by the hydraulic fluid. Make sure the hydraulic filter is changed as recommended and the system is drained and refilled regularly. Flushing is recommended only when the hydraulic fluid is found to be badly contaminated. To flush the system, refill with the recommended hydraulic fluid and operate the equipment to cycle the flushing oil through the system. Operate all valves so that the new oil goes through all the lines. It will probably take several hours of operation to clean a badly contaminated system. When the system operates satisfactorily, drain out the flushing oil, clean or replace the filter and refill the system with hydraulic fluid of the recommended type.

In maintaining those parts of the tractor requiring pressure gun grease, it is a good practice to watch carefully as the periodic greasing is done to see that the fittings are in place and taking grease.

Procedure

1. Lubricate the tractor.
   a. Use the type and grade of grease recommended by the tractor and/or the grease manufacturer.
   b. Wipe all fittings clean before attaching the pressure gun.
   c. Grease the required amount. If the Manual calls for two shots with the grease gun, stop at two shots.
   d. Wipe excess grease from the fittings after removing the gun.
   e. Replace any fittings that are missing or damaged.

Oil Filters

The oil filters used on most tractors are of the replaceable-cartridge type. The element may be paper, folded so that there are hundreds of square inches of filtering surface exposed or it may be of some kind of cloth or waste with a porous case around it. The paper type is probably most common. It is very important to use the filter recommended by the engine manufacturer. The filter element must fit the filter case to function properly.

Oil filters are installed in one of two ways, by-pass or full-flow. The by-pass is least common. The filter is installed in a by-pass line so that only a portion of the oil is forced through the filter at any one time, probably 5 to 10%. When the filter becomes clogged, none of the oil passes through and the filtering stops. In the full-flow type, the filter is installed in the main oil line and all the circulating oil passes through the filter. This system has a by-pass valve to permit the circulation of oil, if the filter is neglected and becomes clogged. The full-flow type filters more oil and thus protects engine parts more completely. The element

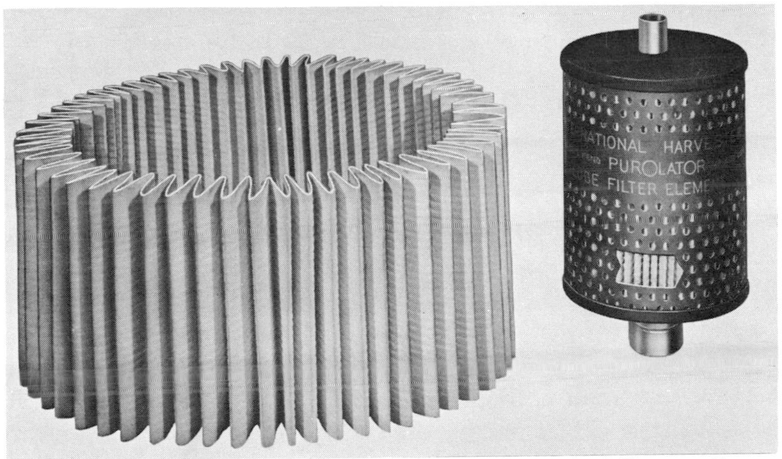

Courtesy International Harvester Co.

Fig. 6-8—One type of oil filter element. Notice the large area of filtering surface.

Courtesy Allis-Chalmers Mfg. Co.

Fig. 6-9—Use the filter recommended by the engine manufacturer.

must be changed regularly so that dirty oil does not by-pass the element and reach engine parts where serious damage could result.

QUESTIONS

1. Why is lubrication probably the most important factor influencing the life of the engine?
2. What duties are performed by the lubricating oil?
3. What is the difference between circulating splash and force-feed oil systems?
4. What should be done to maintain the lubrication system?
5. Why should crankcase oil be drained when the engine is hot?
6. What can be done to help keep dust and dirt out of the lubrication system?

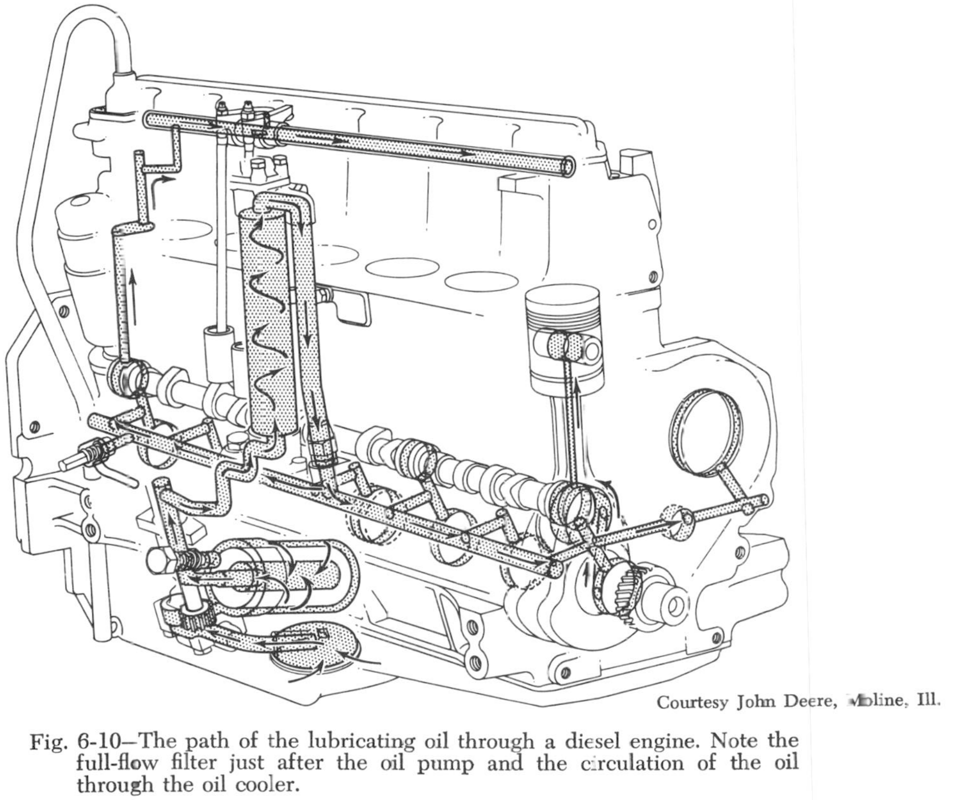

Courtesy John Deere, Moline, Ill.

Fig. 6-10—The path of the lubricating oil through a diesel engine. Note the full-flow filter just after the oil pump and the circulation of the oil through the oil cooler.

7. Why should the oil filter be changed regularly?
8. Why is it important to use the oil filter recommended by the engine manufacturer?
9. Why should the transmission be drained and refilled at least once a year?
10. Why should grease fittings be wiped clean before attaching the pressure gun?
11. What is the difference between a by-pass and a full-flow oil filter?

CHAPTER 7

MAINTAINING THE AIR CLEANER AND CRANKCASE BREATHER

The modern tractor engine must breathe a lot of air, in fact, it requires 9,000 gallons of air to burn one gallon of gasoline. This air is dirty and must be cleaned before it enters the engine. That is the job for the air cleaner. The air cleaner will remove practically all the dust from the air, if it is serviced and maintained regularly. It is well to keep in mind that a half day of

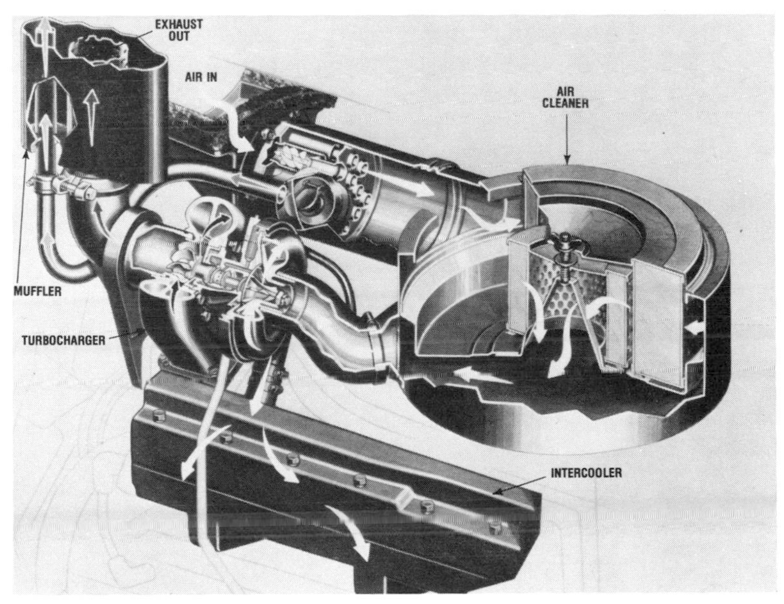

Courtesy Deere & Company Service Publications

Fig. 7-1—Intake-exhaust system on turbocharged, intercooled engine. Note the swirl-type precleaner and the small safety air filter inside the large air filter. Follow the path of the air from the turbocharger through the intercooler.

operation can ruin a tractor engine, if the air cleaner is not doing its job.

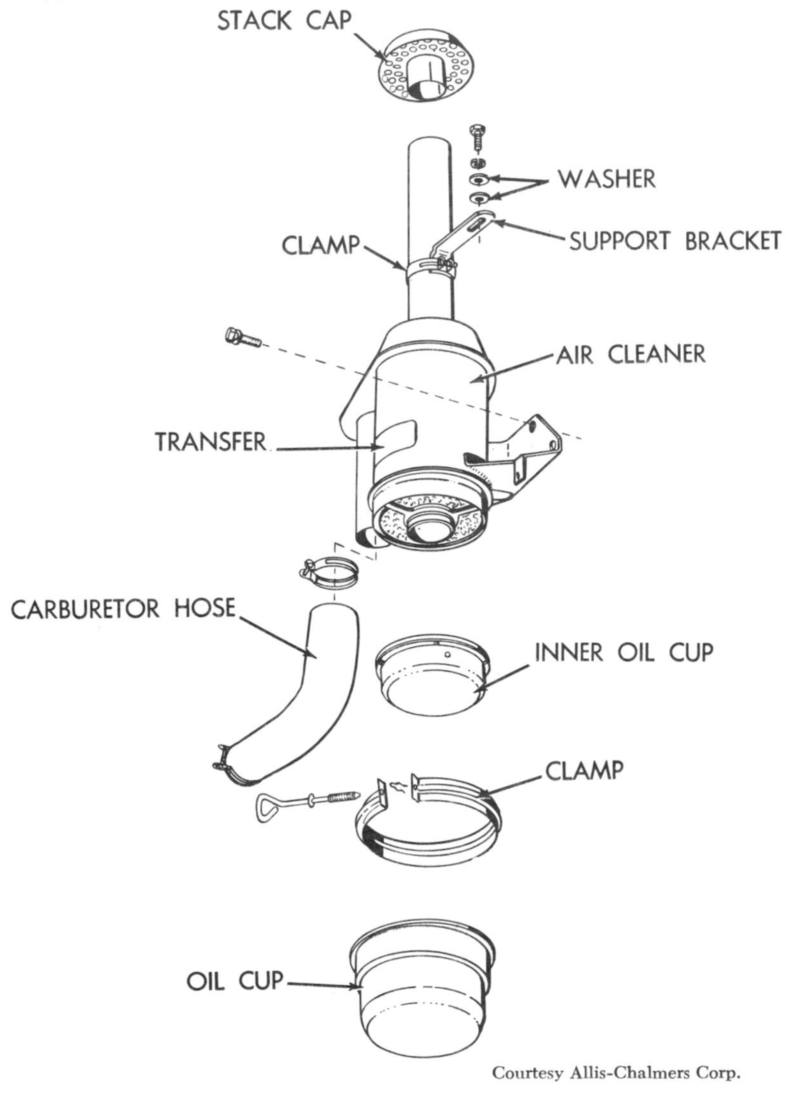

Courtesy Allis-Chalmers Corp.

Fig. 7-2—The parts of an air cleaner.

The maintenance of the air cleaner consists mainly of removing the cup, cleaning it and refilling with new oil, but there is more to the air cleaner than the oil cup. The intake stack, cap, pipes and hose connections also need attention. A leak in the pipe or hose connections can permit dust to be drawn into the system and by-pass the air cleaner. All these connections **must** be **absolutely** air tight.

Courtesy John Deere, Moline, Ill.

Fig. 7-3—Volume of fuel and air needed for a gasoline engine. It takes about 90,000 gallons of air to burn 10 gallons of gasoline in a tractor engine.

Procedure

1. Remove the air cleaner oil cup.
2. Empty and clean the cup.
3. While the cup is off, check the intake stack.
   a. Remove the cap and clean the stack.
   b. If the stack is bent, straighten it.
4. Clean the cap.

Courtesy American Oil Co.

Fig. 7-4—The top part of the air cleaner stack and the pre-cleaner cap were badly plugged.

5. Check the pipe between cleaner and carburetor.
   a. Check the pipe for holes.
   b. Check the hose connections for holes. Replace, if cracked or soft.
   c. Check the hose clamps.
6. Check the wire mesh in the cleaner for trash. Clean it, if dirty.
7. Refill the oil cup with new oil of the recommended viscosity. Refill only to the oil line. Never fill too full, especially on diesel tractors. Too high an oil level could result in a runaway engine, if the oil is drawn into the engine.

While checking the air cleaner, check the rest of the system—the intake manifold, the carburetor, and any place where dust could be drawn into the intake system.

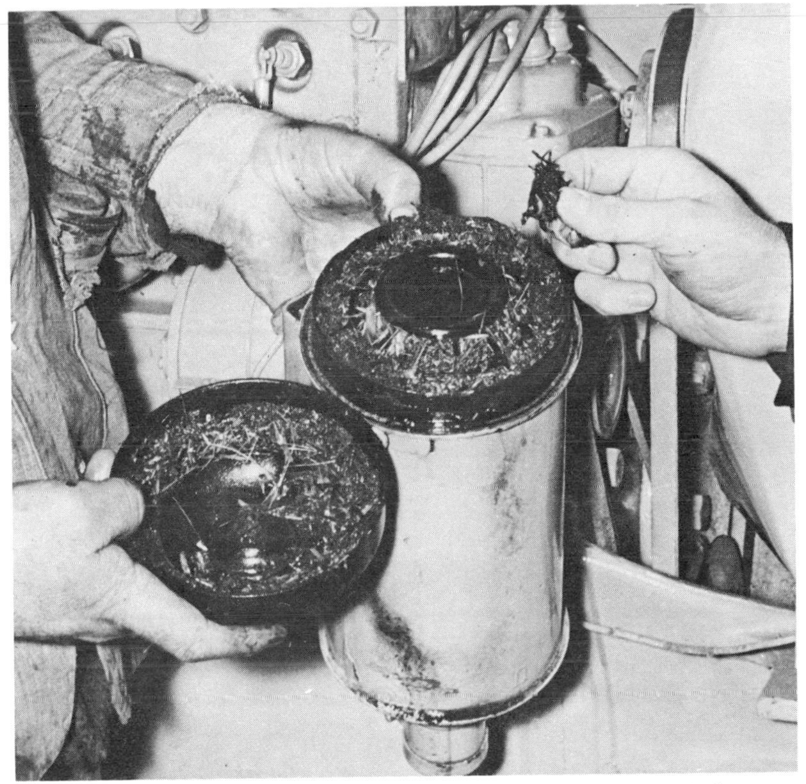

Courtesy American Oil Co.

Fig. 7-5—This air cleaner was almost plugged with hay and straw. Note the straw on the screen. Was this air cleaner serviced daily?

Courtesy John Deere, Moline, Ill.

Fig. 7-6--Diesel engine air cleaner. Note the screen to keep oil from being drawn into the engine.

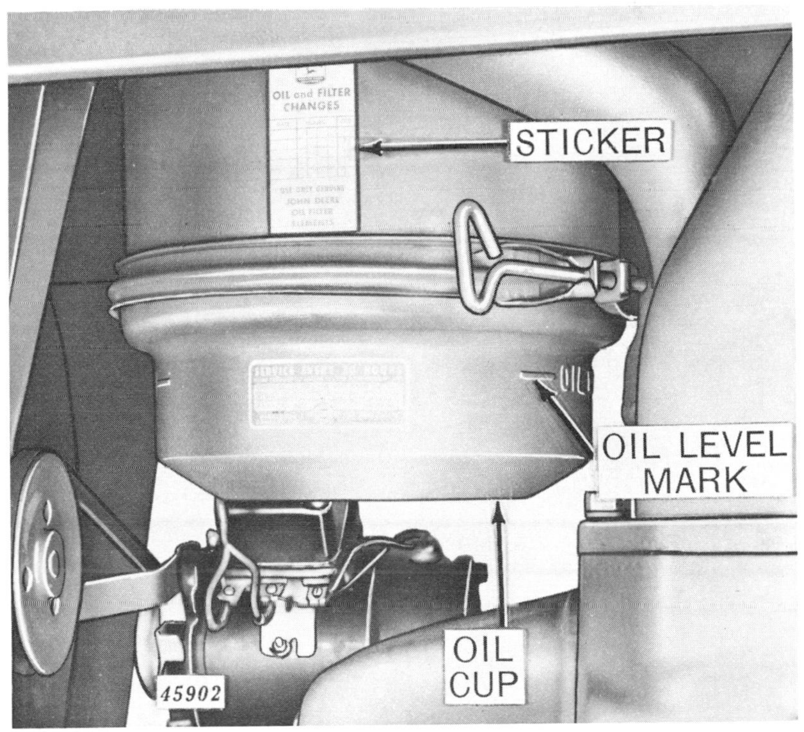

Courtesy John Deere, Moline, Ill.

Fig. 7-7—Diesel engine air cleaner. Never fill above the oil level mark.

Courtesy J. I. Case Co.

Fig. 7-8—One method of cleaning the intake stack.

Procedure

1. Check the intake manifold gasket for leaks.
   a. If a leak is suspected, run the engine and place a few drops of oil on the gasket to see if it is sucked into the engine. If the gasket is bad, replace it with a new gasket.

Courtesy American Oil Co.

Fig. 7-9–The separating cleaner can be cleaned by partially filling the air cleaner with a safe solvent and shaking it. Hold hands over the openings and leave the cup on.

2. Check the openings in the carburetor where throttle valve and choke valve turn in the bearing. If these are loose, have them repaired by the dealer.
3. Check the carburetor fuel drain.
   a. Inspect the hole in the bottom of the carburetor to see that the small felt or porous bronze filter is in place.

Courtesy International Harvester Co.

Fig. 7-10—A pre-cleaner that attaches to the air cleaner intake stack for extra protection when working under excessively dusty conditions. Use only the type recommended by the engine manufacturer and service regularly.

An attachment that is valuable for dusty conditions is the pre-cleaner. This attaches to the top of the intake stack for the purpose of separating some of the dust and dirt before it reaches the oil bath cleaner and relieves the load on the regular cleaner. Various styles of pre-cleaners are available from the manufacturer of the tractor and from other manufacturers. It is well to check with the dealer before installing a pre-cleaner to make sure the tractor will operate satisfactorily with one installed.

The pre-cleaner will need to be emptied regularly so that it does not become clogged and restrict the air flow to the engine.

Courtesy John Deere, Moline, Ill.

Fig. 7-11—A dry-type air cleaner mounted vertically. Note the dust cup in the operator's left hand.

The dry-type air filter is more common on late model tractors than is the oil bath. It is easier and less messy to service and requires less frequent servicing. It is more efficient at both low and high engine speeds. Servicing consists primarily of emptying

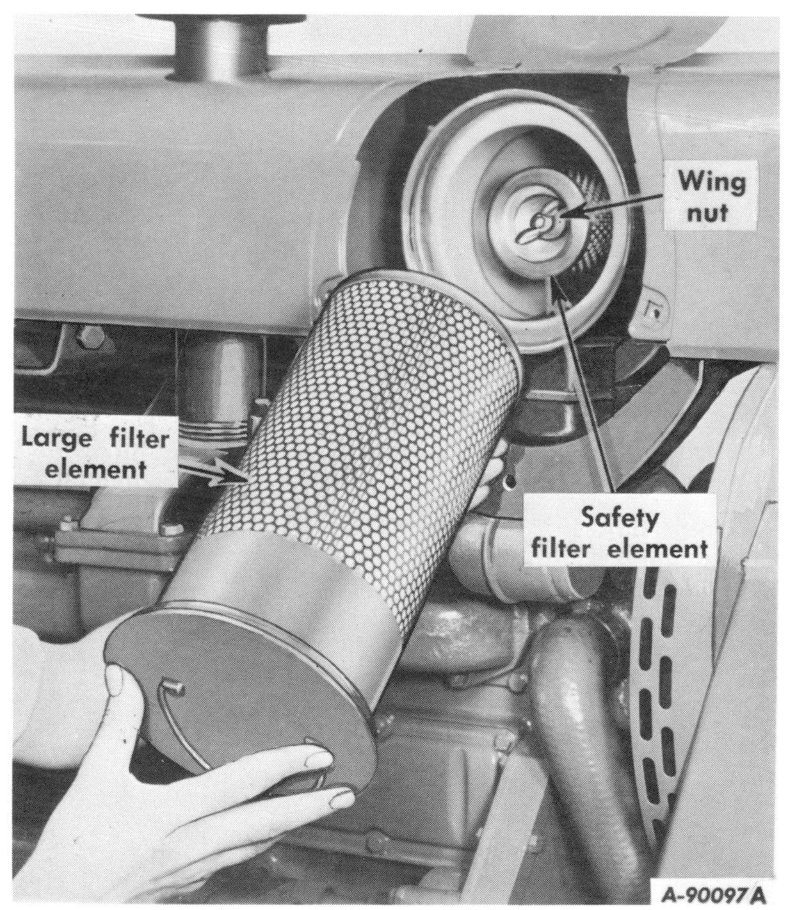

Courtesy International Harvester Co.

Fig. 7-12—A dry-type air cleaner mounted horizontally. Note the safety filter element which is not removed when servicing the larger filter element.

the dust cup on models mounted vertically and checking the automatic dust unloader on some models mounted horizontally.

Eventually the filter element will need to be removed and cleaned.

Procedure

1. Wipe off the outside of the cleaner with a dry cloth.
2. Carefully remove the element.
3. Clean the dust cup and baffle.
4. Clean the element.
   a. Tap the element gently on the palm of your hand to loosen dirt.
   b. If the element is still dirty, blow clean, dry compressed air at low pressure, less than 100 lbs. per square inch, from the inside towards the outside until it is clean.

Courtesy John Deere, Moline, Ill.

Fig. 7-13—A dry-type air cleaner mounted horizontally. Note the air restriction indicator. The indicator will show red when enough dirt has accumulated on the filter to restrict the flow of air.

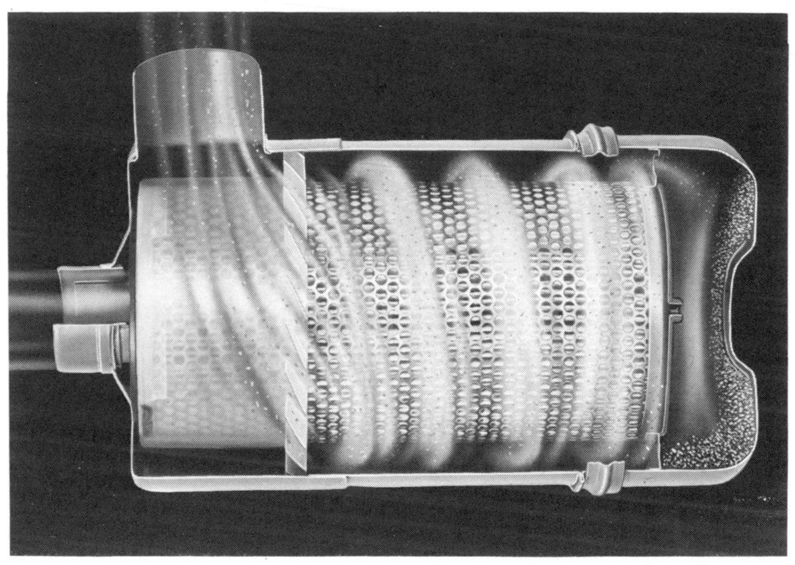

Courtesy John Deere, Moline, Ill.

Fig. 7-14—A cutaway of a dry-type air cleaner. The inlet is at the top, dust cup is at the right, clean air comes out at the left. Note the swirling, separating action caused by the fins. The dust cup must be installed with the slot at the top.

Courtesy Dana Corp., manufacturer of Perfect Circle Piston Rings

Fig. 7-15—Vertical scratches on piston ring faces indicate airborne abrasives are entering the engine.

Courtesy John Deere, Moline, Ill.

Fig. 7-16—A cross-section of one type of crankcase ventilation system. Late model engines have a similar system with a gear-driven air pump that constantly circulates clean air through the crankcase and valve covers.

c. If the element is still dirty or oily, it will need to be washed. Flush the element from the inside with clean water from a hose. Wash the element in a recommended, nonsudsing detergent. Flush from the inside with clean water. Allow the element to dry for 24 hours at room temperature.

5. Inspect for leaks.

   a. Insert a light bulb on the inside and look from the outside for holes or cracks. If any light can be seen, throw the element away.

6. Install the element.
   a. Check the rubber gasket. If it is damaged or missing, install a new element.

The crankcase breather is often neglected because it does not require attention as often as the air cleaner. The breather is very important because it ventilates the crankcase and prevents dust from being drawn into the engine. Failure to keep the breather clean will result in excessive pressure in the crankcase that will force the lubricating oil past seals and promote excessive oil consumption. Lack of ventilation will promote the formation of acids and sludge in the crankcase.

There are many kinds of crankcase breathers. Some are located in the plate covering the push rod chamber. A common type is located in the cap on the valve cover or oil filler tube. Consult your Operator's Manual for the type, location and service recommended. Most breathers contain an element of crimped copper which is oil soaked. Dirt in the air passing this element is

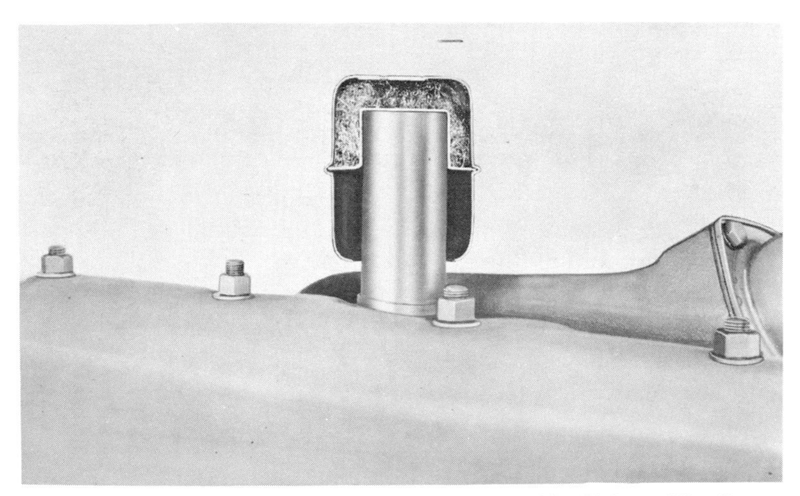

Courtesy Allis-Chalmers Mfg. Co.

Fig. 7-17—One type of crankcase breather cap on the valve cover. Wash this type frequently. When it can no longer be cleaned, replace it.

trapped in the oil and must be removed by washing the element. The element should be cleaned as often as necessary, twice a day in extremely dusty conditions.

Procedure

1. Remove the crankcase breather.
2. Wash the element in kerosene or solvent.
3. Shake the element dry or blow with compressed air.
4. Oil the element and shake off excess oil before replacing it.
5. Replace the element.

Courtesy Massey-Ferguson

Fig. 7-18—A turbocharged diesel tractor that develops 100 PTO hp. with a Category II implement rapid coupler.

QUESTIONS

1. How much air is used to burn one gallon of gasoline?
2. What maintenance is necessary on the air cleaner?
3. Why are tight hose connections so important on the air cleaner?
4. Trace the path the air travels in a gasoline engine and in a diesel engine.
5. What happens if there is a leak between the air cleaner and the carburetor on a gasoline engine?
6. What happens if there is a leak between the air cleaner and intake manifold on a diesel engine?
7. Why is it important that there be no leaks around the intake manifold?
8. Why are the screens or baffles so important in a diesel engine air cleaner?
9. What could happen if too much oil were placed in a diesel engine air cleaner?
10. Why should the intake stack be cleaned occasionally?
11. Why is a pre-cleaner sometimes used on the air cleaner?
12. What servicing does the pre-cleaner require?
13. Why should you check to see if the manufacturer recommends the use of a pre-cleaner?
14. What is the purpose of the crankcase breather?
15. What happens in the engine when the crankcase breather becomes dirty and partially clogged?
16. How should the crankcase breather be serviced?

CHAPTER 8

MAINTAINING THE COOLING SYSTEM

Maintaining the cooling system of a modern tractor engine is very important and should start with the care of the new tractor. The cooling system will probably function quite well for the first few years, but if neglected, will eventually cease to function efficiently and overheating and damage to the engine will occur.

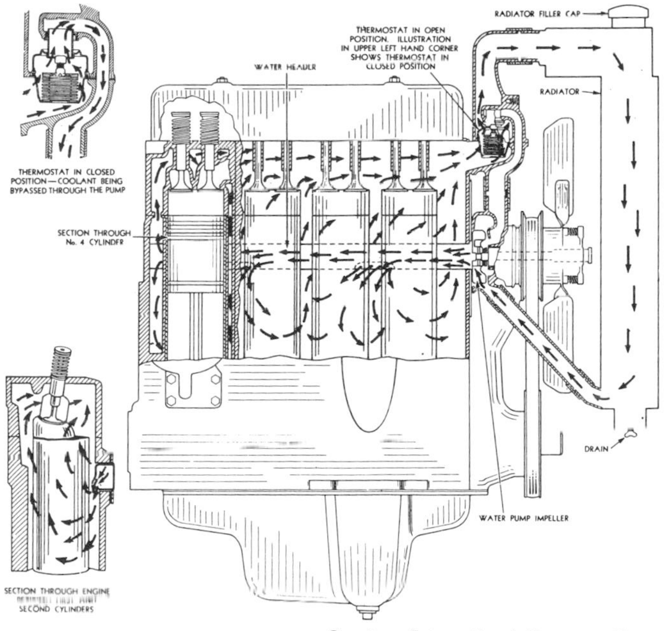

Courtesy International Harvester Co.

Fig. 8-1—Cutaway drawing of a cooling system. Note the path of the water through the block, head, thermostat and radiator. Note the illustration in the upper left hand corner. When the thermostat is closed, the coolant circulates through the block for a quick warm-up. You *must* use the correct thermostat when replacing this type.

The cooling system does two things: (1) prevents the engine from overheating; (2) keeps the engine at the proper operating temperature for efficiency and long life.

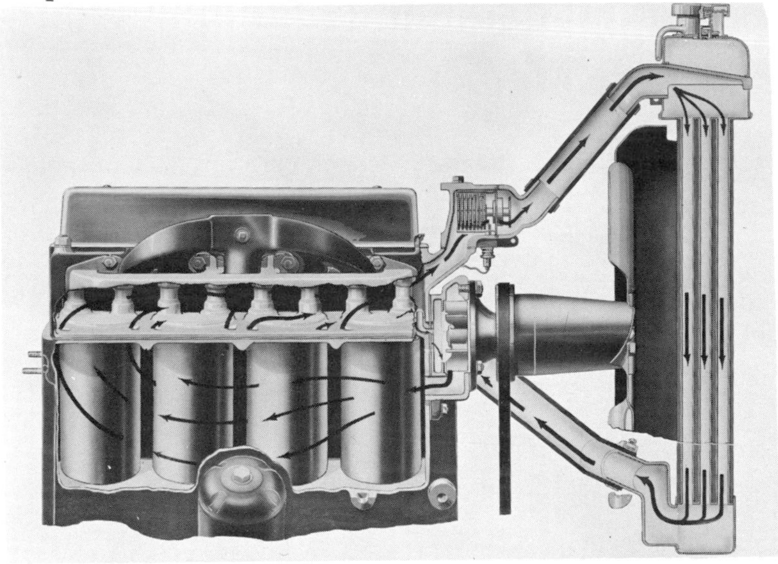

Courtesy Massey-Ferguson

Fig. 8-2—Cutaway drawing of a cooling system showing the thermostat and pressure cap.

The importance of keeping the engine at the correct operating temperature is probably not understood as well by the average tractor operator as is the importance of preventing overheating.

Correct Operating Temperature

An engine cannot last long or operate efficiently unless it is operated at the correct temperature. There seems to be a rather common belief that an engine that runs cool is running efficiently and will last a long time. This is a false belief.

The engine should operate at a temperature high enough so that the water will not quite boil away in the top of the radiator. At this temperature, wear is reduced to a minimum, fuel consumption is reduced and power is increased. Most tractor operators have observed the lack of power with a cold engine when starting to plow or do some similar heavy work.

The cooling system on a tractor must have enough cooling capacity to prevent the engine from overheating under heavy loads in hot weather. When operated under light loads in cold weather, the cooling system tends to keep the engine too cool. Under this condition, the lower part of the radiator should be covered enough to bring the temperature up to the proper operating range. Radiator shutters are available as an accessory on some tractors for this purpose.

A cold engine wears rapidly and operates inefficiently with high fuel consumption and loss of power. Sludge formation and corrosion of engine parts takes place, so an attempt should always be made to get the engine up to the correct operating temperature.

Courtesy American Oil Co.

Fig. 8-3—Ample air for cooling cannot pass through a radiator filled with trash.

Overheating

Overheating is indicated by rapid boiling away of the water, knocking and loss of power. There are many causes of overheating and rapid damage to the engine can occur when it does take place.

Courtesy John Deere, Moline, Ill.

Fig. 8-4—CAUTION: Remove the radiator filler cap only when the coolant temperature is below the boiling point (in the "N" range on the water temperature gauge). Then loosen the cap slightly to the stop to relieve pressure before removing the cap completely.

If an engine does overheat, it should not be shut down immediately or serious damage may result. Idle the engine a few minutes to permit exhaust valves and pistons to cool, so that expanded pistons will not seize and valves will not warp or crack.

Causes of Overheating

1. Low water level in the radiator.
2. Using a fuel that knocks.
3. A slipping fan belt.
4. Overloading of the tractor.
5. Clogged radiator fins.

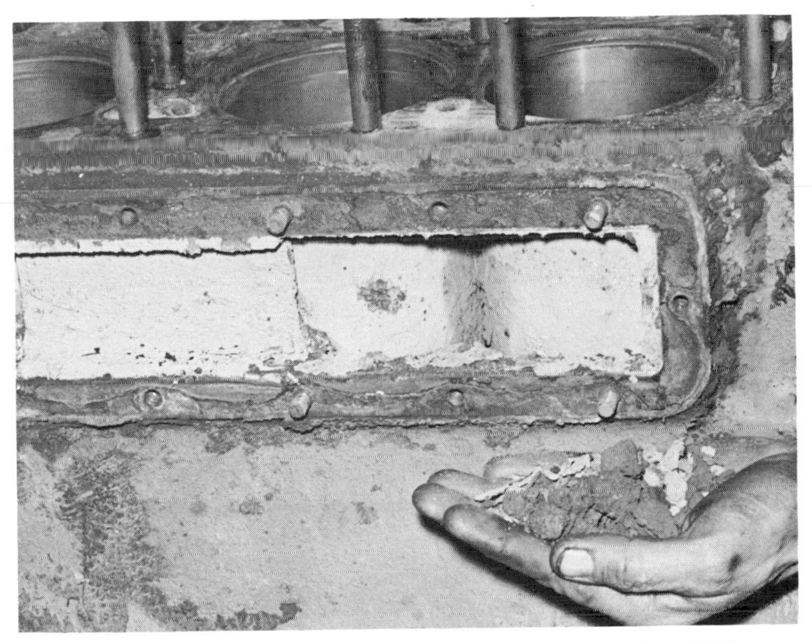

Courtesy American Oil Co.

Fig. 8-5—Lime deposits like this should be removed with a strong cooling system cleaner to help prevent piston ring scoring and short valve life. Use soft water in the cooling system and fix leaks promptly.

6. Collapsed radiator hoses.
7. Lime accumulation in the cooling system.
8. Ignition out of time.
9. Carburetor out of adjustment (too lean a mixture).
10. Radiator partly covered by shutters or other cover in warm weather.
11. Faulty water pump.
12. Thermostat stuck closed.

COOLING SYSTEMS

There are two general methods of cooling an engine, air cooling and water cooling (liquid cooling).

Air Cooling

Air cooling is used on some power units on balers and other field machines and on one cylinder garden tractor and lawn mower engines. In an air cooled engine, a strong blast of air from a fan is directed by shrouds to fins surrounding the cylinders. The fan is usually incorporated in the flywheel.

Maintenance of an air cooling system consists of cleaning dirt, chaff and dust from the fins and intake screen and keeping the shrouds in place and repaired so the air is directed to the fins. This cleaning will need to be done as often as dirt accumulates, once a day, sometimes oftener and under clean conditions only occasionally. Failure to keep the fins and screen clean will permit hot spots to occur in the cylinder walls with damage to the rings and walls as a result.

Courtesy John Deere, Moline, Ill.

Fig. 8-6—Cooling system components.

Water Cooling

There are two general systems used in water cooling. The simplest type is the thermo-syphon system in which the hot water rises to the top of the water jacket and on up the system to the radiator. As air is drawn through the radiator by the fan, the water is cooled and moves down through the radiator and back into the bottom of the block. An impeller may be used to assist the circulation of the water.

The forced circulation system is the most common type on modern tractor engines. In this system, a pump forces the water to circulate through the water jacket and radiator. A thermostat is usually located in the system to block the flow of water to the radiator until the block is warmed up. This aids in a quick warm-up of the engine and reduces the wear that takes place before the block is up to operating temperature.

Courtesy American Oil Co.

Fig. 8-7—This tractor thermostat is standing open because of a cracked bellows. With this in the system the engine will not warm up quickly or be kept at the correct operating temperature.

Thermostats

When the water in a cooling system fails to heat up as quickly as it should, the thermostat is usually at fault. Two types of thermostats are used, the bimetallic strip and the bellows. One type has a bimetallic strip which expands when heated thus opening the valve. The other type uses a bellows, filled under a partial vacuum with a liquid having a low boiling point. When the liquid in the bellows is heated, it expands and opens the valve. In each of these two types, a valve is held closed until the water reaches the temperature at which the thermostat has been designed to open, usually in the range of 165 to 185 degrees F. When the thermostat opens, water is permitted to flow through the radiator. In cold weather the radiator may cool the water to below the full open temperature of the thermostat causing it to partially close to restrict the flow and keep the water at the desired temperature. A faulty thermostat usually sticks open or opens at a temperature that is too low. Occasionally a thermostat sticks closed and the engine overheats quickly.

An engine should not be operated without a thermostat. The engine will not be maintained at the proper operating temperature. In some systems a by-pass circulates the coolant through the block until the solution is hot enough to cause the thermostat to open, closing off this passageway and causing circulation through the radiator. If the thermostat is left out of this system, the coolant will by-pass the radiator and cause the engine to overheat.

Anti-freeze Solutions

Tractors operated during periods when the temperature is below freezing should either be drained at the end of each day, or filled with an anti-freeze solution. There is probably less danger of damage to the tractor if an anti-freeze solution is used. When the practice of draining the tractor each day is followed, there is always the chance that some water will remain in the block or radiator and freeze. There is also the possibility that someone will forget to drain the system some evening. The cost of replacing a cracked block would buy enough anti-freeze to supply a tractor for many years.

Only two types of anti-freeze should be considered for use in tractor engines—an alcohol type or a permanent type. Tractor engines usually operate at a temperature above the boiling point of alcohol so the permanent type is recommended by most tractor manufacturers. The term "permanent" means the solution will not boil away and should not be interpreted to mean that it is good for use year after year. Permanent type anti-freeze should not be used more than one year. It should be removed in the summer, because it is not as efficient for cooling as water and the rust inhibitor included in the solution is not effective the second year. If permanent anti-freeze is left in year after year, damage to the system is almost sure to occur.

The cooling system must be free of leaks when permanent type anti-freeze is installed. This solution will leak where water will not and a leak into the engine may result in seizing of engine parts. Some tractor manufacturers recommend that a good radiator sealer be added when permanent type anti-freeze is used as an insurance against leaks. Follow the recommendations in the Operator's Manual on this. Be sure head bolts are drawn down to the recommended torque and that all gaskets are in good condition.

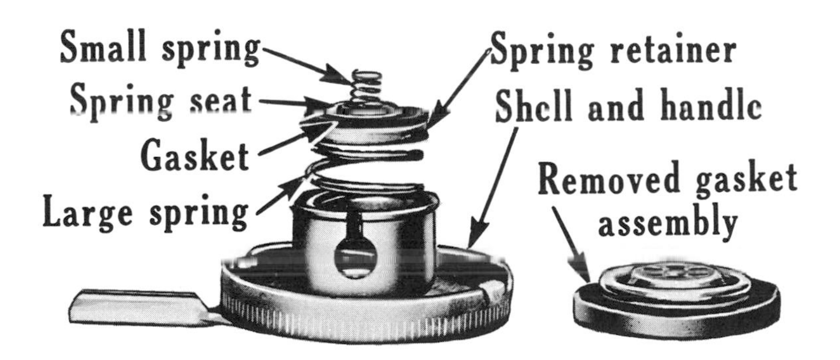

Courtesy International Harvester Co.

Fig. 8-8—The parts of a typical pressure radiator cap for a tractor.

Atmospheric and Pressure Systems

Water cooling systems may be open to atmospheric pressure or operated under a few pounds pressure to raise the boiling point of water to about 230°F. A pressure radiator cap is used to place the system under pressure. The cap is constructed with a coil spring that holds a plate down against the opening in the top of the radiator until the pressure builds up to the specified pounds per square inch, usually 4 to 7 pounds. When the pressure exceeds this, the valve opens, permitting pressure to escape through the overflow pipe which connects to the radiator neck above the valve seat. The center of the valve cap has a small relief valve which opens to relieve the slight vacuum when the system cools down to prevent the radiator from collapsing. It is obvious that both these valves must be kept in good operating condition to prevent damage to the system. Check the condition of the cap each time

Courtesy American Oil Co.

Fig. 8-9—A pressure cap with a damaged gasket. This should be repaired or replaced because it cannot hold pressure.

Courtesy Massey-Ferguson

Fig. 8-10—Remove the grill and brush the radiator fins clean with a soft brush occasionally.

it is removed and repair the gaskets or replace the cap when it isn't operating correctly.

Procedures

Follow the directions given in the manufacturer's Operator's Manual, if at all possible. They are specific for your tractor, rather than general.

Warm Weather

1. Check the radiator twice daily, refill with clean, soft water.
2. Check for leaks and repair them as soon as located.
3. Brush, blow or wash dust, dirt, and chaff out of the radiator fins as it accumulates. Be careful not to break fins loose from the tubes or to puncture the tubes.

4. Adjust fan belt.
   Fan-belt adjusting devices vary. Check the manual for specific instructions.
   a. Adjust V belts so that the belt can be pushed $\frac{1}{2}$ to $\frac{3}{4}$ inch out of line with the thumb.

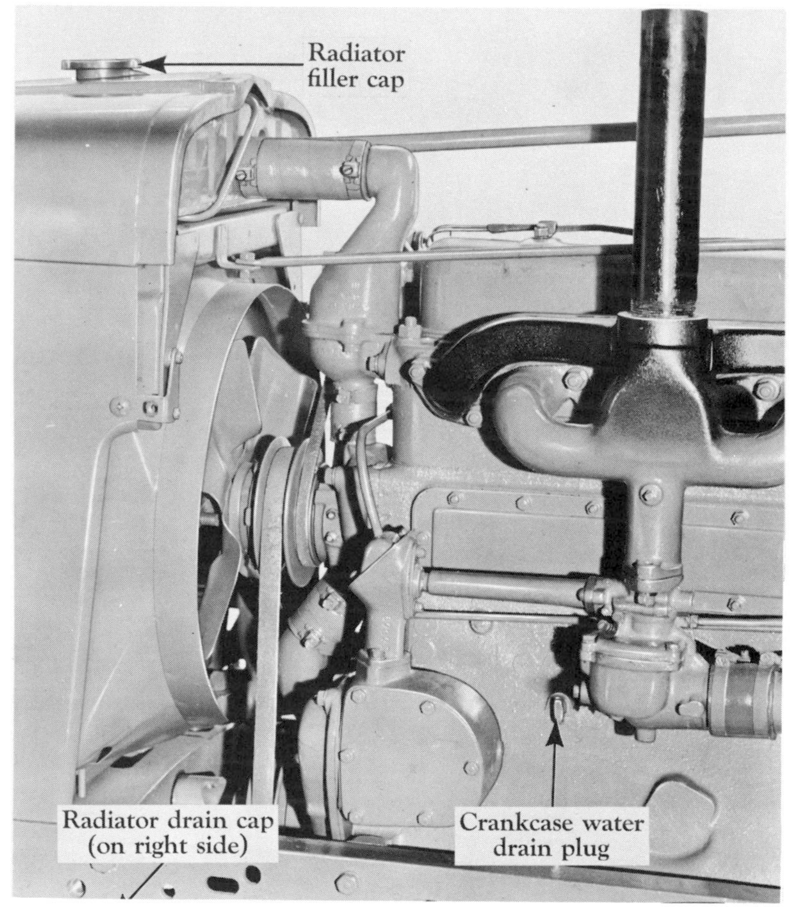

Courtesy International Harvester Co.

Fig. 8-11—Side view of a typical tractor engine showing location of radiator and block drains.

b. Check to see that the inside of the belt is not riding the bottom of the V pulley. Some pulleys are split so that the width is adjustable. In such cases, move the flanges together enough to raise the belt from the bottom of the groove. If the pulley is not adjustable, replace the worn belt with a new one.

5. Drain and flush the cooling system once or twice a year.

Method 1:

a. Remove the thermostat.
b. Refill radiator and run the engine for a few minutes to stir up the rust or sediment.
c. Stop the engine and drain entire system quickly.
d. Replace drain plugs or close petcocks and refill system with soft water and washing soda (one pound for each 2½ gallons of water).

Courtesy Massey-Ferguson

Fig. 8-12—Remove the hood and grill to thoroughly service the cooling system.

NOTE: The washing soda will dissolve only in warm water.

e. Run the engine until the water becomes hot.
f. Drain the system.
g. Flush the system with clean water until the water comes out clean.
h. Replace thermostat.
i. Fill the system with clean, soft water or with anti-freeze solution for winter operation.

NOTE: When filling the system with water, add a good, reputable commercial rust inhibitor. This will help protect the system and reduce rusting.

Method 2:

When cooling system deposits are quite heavy, a more drastic cleaner may be needed to dissolve the lime deposits.

a. Remove the thermostat.
b. Refill radiator and run the engine a few minutes to stir up rust and sediment.
c. Stop the engine and drain entire system quickly.
d. Fill the system with a solution made as follows:
   - 5 parts commercial muriatic acid
   - 1 part commercial formaldehyde
   - 42 parts clean soft water
e. Run at operating temperature for two or three hours.
f. Drain the system.
g. Refill system with water to which has been added 1 pound of lye, run for a few minutes.
h. Drain and flush thoroughly with clean water.
i. Fill the system with clean, soft water or with an anti-freeze solution for winter operation. Add a good commercial rust inhibitor for summer operation. Anti-freeze contains a rust inhibitor good for one season, if it is a permanent type. (This procedure courtesy C. N. Hinkle, American Oil Co.)

Courtesy John Deere, Moline, Ill.

Fig. 8-13—Never pour hot water in a cold engine or cold water in a hot engine.

Courtesy John Deere, Moline, Ill.

Fig. 8-14—CAUTION: Never pour hot water into a cold engine or cold water into a hot engine. You may crack the head or the cylinder block. Do not operate the tractor without water for even a few minutes.

WARNING—Muriatic acid, formaldehyde, and lye are poisonous and extreme caution should be used to keep them away from children and animals. Do not leave any of these solutions, or any poison solution in soft drink bottles because of the temptation for children to drink them.

Method 3:

Use a good commercial cooling system cleaner *according to directions.*

6. Inspect and replace hoses before they deteriorate and collapse.
   a. Pinch the hose to see if the walls feel thin and weak. Inspect the inside of the hose if it doesn't seem right.
   b. Loosen one hose clamp and remove one end of the hose. Loose or wrinkled lining indicates that the hose should be replaced.
7. When the thermostat is out, check to see if it opens correctly.
   a. Place the thermostat in hot water and measure the temperature of the water with a thermometer to determine the temperature at which the thermostat starts to open

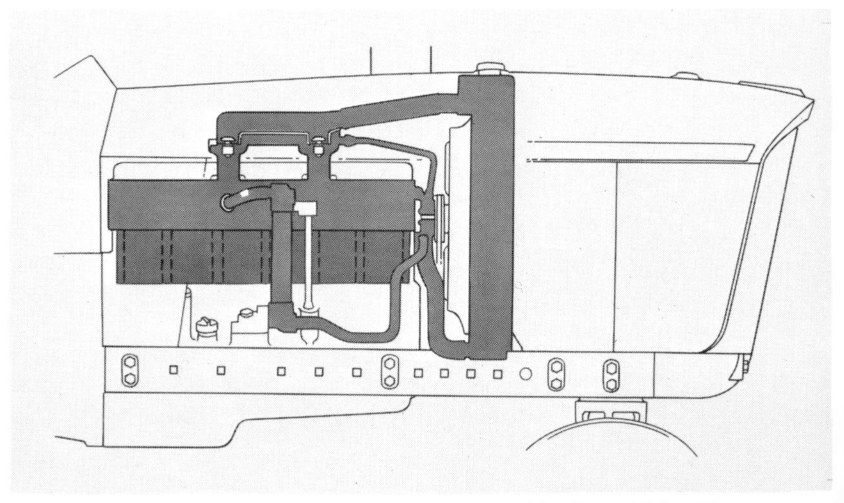

Courtesy John Deere, Moline, Ill.

Fig. 8-15—The cooling system of a 6 cylinder engine. Note how the two thermostats cause the coolant to circulate through the block until the engine is warm.

and is fully open. Replace it, if it doesn't operate at the temperature desired.

WARNING—If you put **hot** water in a **cold** engine or **cold** water in a **hot** engine, the head or block may crack. Do not operate the tractor without water for even a minute or two.

Courtesy John Deere, Moline, Ill.

Fig. 8-16—A large row crop tractor developing over 125 PTO hp.

QUESTIONS

1. Why is the maintenance of the cooling system important in a new engine?
2. Trace the path the water takes through the engine when the thermostat is closed.
3. Trace the path of the water through the engine when the thermostat is open.
4. The engine should not be operated with the thermostat removed. Why is this important?
5. How does the thermostat keep the engine at the proper operating temperature?
6. What maintenance is necessary on the cooling system of an air cooled engine?
7. What damage can occur in an air cooled engine from dirt accumulation in the cooling fins?
8. What maintenance is necessary on the cooling system of a liquid cooled engine?
9. Why is a "permanent" type anti-freeze usually recommended for tractor engines?
10. Why should "permanent" type anti-freeze be drained in the summer and not be re-used?

CHAPTER 9

MAINTAINING THE FUEL SYSTEM

The most important item in maintaining the fuel system is the use of clean fuel. Clean fuel in a diesel engine is absolutely necessary and cannot be overemphasized. Fuel that is as clean as possible should be purchased, placed in a clean tank and transferred to the tractor with a minimum of handling to reduce the chance for contamination with dirt or water.

Water is always a problem in a fuel system and may come from any one of several sources—water already in the fuel, water which has leaked into the storage tank or into the tractor fuel tank, and water that condenses out of the air inside the tank. Condensation is the most common source of water.

Condensation occurs when moisture laden air comes in contact with a cool surface. A tractor fuel tank cools at night, the moisture in the air above the fuel inside the tank condenses on the cool sides of the tank and enters the fuel. The simplest way to prevent this is to fill the tank with fuel at the end of the day. This will exclude air from the inside of the tank. Do not fill the tank on a hot tractor because of danger from fire. Wait a reasonable length of time for the tractor to cool before refueling.

GASOLINE ENGINE SYSTEM

The fuel system on a gasoline engine consists of a fuel tank, sediment bowl, a fuel pump (on some tractors), fuel lines and strainers, a carburetor, and an intake manifold.

The maintenance of the fuel system is essentially that of inspecting, checking and making repairs or adjustments, as they are needed. If clean fuel is used, only infrequently will any repair jobs need to be done.

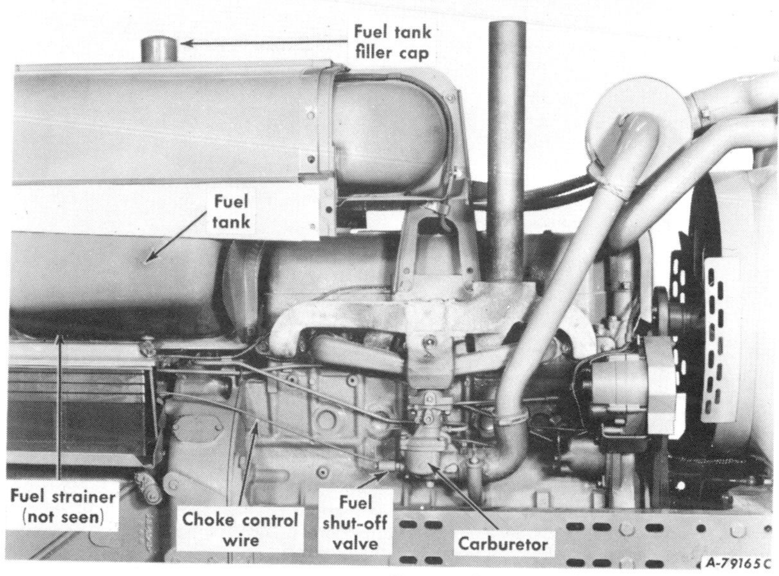

Courtesy International Harvester Co.

Fig. 9-1—Side view of a tractor showing the fuel system.

Fuel Tank

The tank may need to be cleaned occasionally. If sediment and water collect often in the sediment bowl, it indicates dirt in the tank and the tank will need to be drained and flushed with clean fuel.

Procedure

1. Shut off fuel.
2. Loosen jam nut holding sediment bowl in place.
3. Twist bowl to loosen it.
4. Remove bowl, strainer and gasket.
5. Turn on the fuel and catch in a container to reduce fire hazard.
6. Splash clean fuel around inside the tank and drain to remove dirt.

Courtesy International Harvester Co.

Fig. 9-2—Keep vent holes in the filter cap open.

7. Wash strainer in clean fuel, wipe bowl clean.
8. Replace strainer, gasket and bowl.
9. Fill tank with clean fuel.

If the tank becomes rusty enough so that rust is getting into the sediment bowl frequently, the tank will need to be removed and replaced with a new tank. This will not be necessary very often.

Sediment Bowl and Fuel Strainer

Small particles of dirt and water are trapped in the sediment bowl to prevent clogging of the small jets in the carburetor. As often as dirt or water accumulates in the bowl, it will need to be removed and cleaned.

Use a metal or heat resistant bowl when picking corn or when there is danger of dirt and leaves collecting around the bowl and catching fire. Ordinary glass bowls will break and fuel will feed the fire.

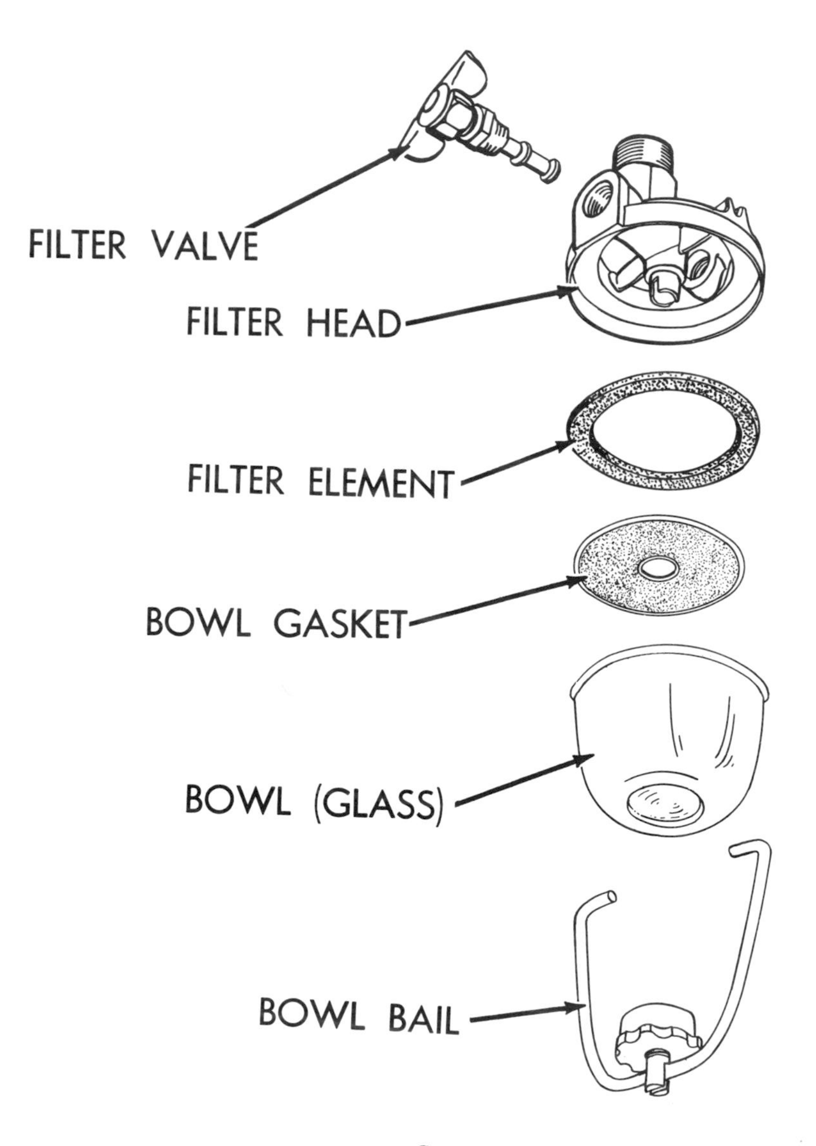

Courtesy International Harvester Co.

Fig. 9-3—Parts of the sediment bowl and fuel strainer.

Procedure

1. Shut off fuel at the tank.
2. Loosen jam nut holding bowl in place.
3. Twist bowl to loosen it without damaging gasket.
4. Remove bowl, strainer and gasket.
5. Wash strainer in fuel, wipe bowl clean.
6. Replace gasket, strainer and bowl. (A new gasket is usually needed to prevent a leak.)
7. Turn the fuel on, as soon as all air is out of the bowl, tighten jam nut enough to stop the fuel from leaking.

Fuel Pump

If the system uses a fuel pump, it will be found between the tank and the carburetor. There isn't much maintenance that the operator can do on the fuel pump other than check to see that it is operating and replace it with a new or rebuilt pump when it fails.

Failure of the fuel pump will be indicated by: failure of the engine to start, loss of power at high speeds or under load, high gasoline consumption, or a spray of gasoline coming from the top of the fuel pump. A ruptured diaphragm in the pump may permit fuel to be pumped into the crankcase. Any time the crankcase oil is diluted excessively with fuel or the oil level rises above normal, the fuel pump should be checked for leaks. The operation of the pump can be checked by loosening the fuel line from the carburetor and cranking the engine. Fuel should spurt from the fuel line, if the pump is working.

When the pump fails, remove it and exchange it for a new or rebuilt pump at the dealer's. Check with the dealer to find out the procedure for installing the new pump without damage to the pump arm or the camshaft against which it operates.

Fuel Lines and Strainers

Fittings at the ends of fuel lines will occasionally start to leak as a result of vibration. Usually a slight tightening of the fitting will stop the leak and this should be done as soon as the leak is detected in order to prevent further damage to the fitting. If tight-

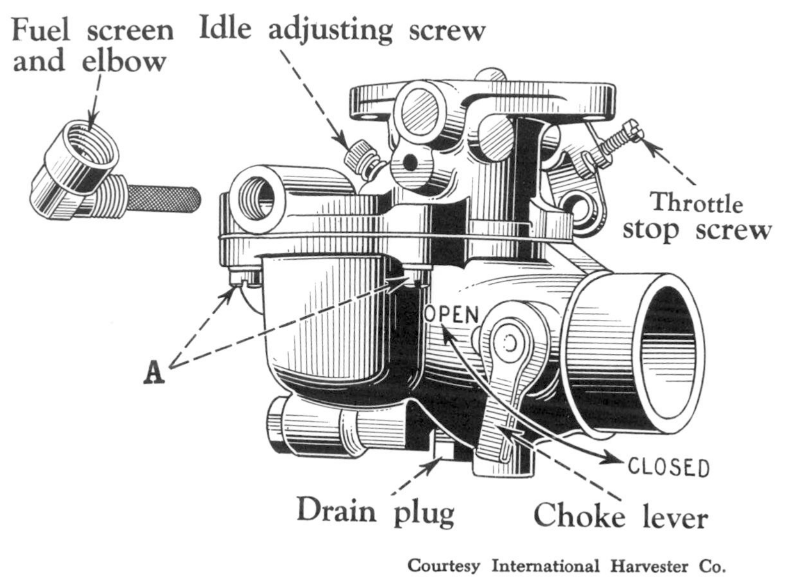

Courtesy International Harvester Co.

Fig. 9-4—A typical tractor carburetor. Note the fuel strainer.

ening doesn't stop the leak, replace the fitting or the line and fittings.

A strainer is often located in the carburetor at the end of the fuel line. Occasionally this strainer should be cleaned to remove any sediment trapped there. Follow the directions in the Operator's Manual for cleaning this strainer. Be careful in replacing the line to not cross-thread the fitting.

Carburetor

The chief job of the carburetor is to mix fuel and air for delivery into the combustion chamber.

Fuel, for greatest power, is usually mixed with air at the ratio of 1:12.85 to 1:16.15. The size of this job can be visualized best by considering that for each 1 gallon of gasoline more than 9,000 cu. ft. of air is required, or the air that could be contained in a 16′ by 50′ silo. The exact proportion of fuel and air needed by the engine varies with the speed, load, temperature, rate of acceleration, and other factors. Performance and economy are always important to the owner. The carburetor is a precision instrument of a somewhat complicated design. Generally, the carburetor will do its job without trouble for long periods, provided it has clean fuel of the proper kind and clean air to mix with it. The operator should usually adopt a "hands off" policy for the carburetor except for minor adjustments. For complete overhaul and rebuilding, the carburetor should be taken to a specialist.

Unnecessary adjustment of the carburetor can result in loss of power, high fuel consumption and burned valves.

Too lean a mixture results in poor economy because of loss of power, poor acceleration, and a tendency to burn valves and spark plugs.

Too rich a mixture results in wasted fuel and in piston and ring wear due to the washing off of lubricating oil, dilution and increased carbon formation.

The maintenance of the carburetor will consist chiefly of checking nuts and bolts for tightness and making idle speed, idle mixture and load mixture adjustment.

Check the bolts or nuts that fasten the carburetor to the manifold. Tighten these when they are loose.

Occasionally tighten the screws which fasten the fuel bowl to the fuel bowl cover. Keep these screws tight to prevent air leaks.

Idle Speed Adjustment

The idle speed adjustment is a stop screw that determines how far the throttle valve will close when the throttle lever is at the full idling position. Many engines have been ruined by idling them too slowly. Check the Operator's Manual for the correct idle speed for the tractor being adjusted.

The adjustment procedure is to, first have the tractor warm, then close the throttle and screw the idle speed adjustment in or out until the desired idle speed is obtained. A speed counter or tachometer will be needed, to set the speed correctly.

Idle Mixture Adjustment

With the engine warmed up and idling at the correct speed, the idle mixture adjustment can be made.

Turn the idle adjusting screw out until the engine runs roughly, then turn the screw in until the engine runs smoothly; this should be the correct idle mixture adjustment. The correct adjustment will usually be found with the adjusting screw turned out one to one and a quarter turns.

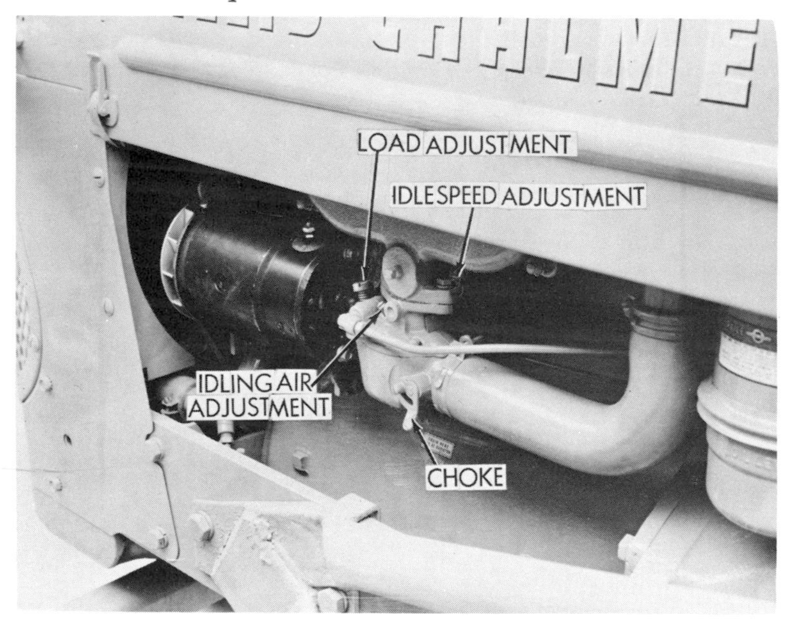

Courtesy Allis-Chalmers Mfg. Co.

Fig. 9-5—A tractor carburetor showing the location of the adjustments.

Screwing the idle mixture screw *in* usually restricts the *air* and gives a *richer* mixture. Screwing it *out* gives a *leaner* mixture.

Load Mixture Adjustment

The smaller tractors usually have no provision on the carburetor for making an adjustment of the load mixture. A fixed jet is used and the only way to change the adjustment is to change jets.

On the larger tractors, the load mixture is adjustable by means of a screw adjustment. Check the Operator's Manual for the adjustment procedure and for the location of the load mixture adjustment screw.

The procedure is to have the tractor warm, open the throttle and screw the load mixture screw in, until the engine mis-fires, then turn the screw out until the engine runs smoothly. Now place the tractor under load and observe how it reacts. If there is backfiring through the carburetor and the engine tends to stall, the mixture is still too lean. Back the adjustment out about an eighth of a turn and place the tractor under load again. Repeat this until the tractor takes the load smoothly.

Screwing the load mixture screw *in* usually restricts the *fuel* flow and gives a *leaner* mixture. Screwing it *out* gives a *richer* mixture.

Courtesy John Deere, Moline, Ill.

Fig. 9-6—Caution: Never adjust the carburetor while tractor is moving.

Obviously, the load adjustment should be made with the tractor under load, but do not attempt to walk beside the tractor and make the adjustment while the tractor is moving because of the danger of tripping and falling under the wheel. The procedure given is much safer although it takes longer.

It is not necessary to be constantly changing the carburetor settings; in fact, it is not advisable to do this. Once the carburetor is set correctly, adjustment should not be necessary unless the load changes or the fuel quality changes radically. If the adjustment is made for heavy loads and the tractor is operated on light loads, the mixture will be too rich which will waste fuel and cause unnecessary wear and damage from oil dilution. Operating with a mixture that is too lean may result in overheating, loss of power and high exhaust valve temperatures that will burn the valves. There is no economy in using a lean mixture.

Manifold

Check the manifold for leaks and tighten manifold bolts, if leaks are found. Replace manifold gaskets, if tightening does not stop the leaks.

Governor

The engine speed control lever is not connected to the carburetor throttle valve, but is connected to a governor. As the speed control lever is moved it changes the tension on a spring in the governor and an arm from the governor then opens or closes the throttle valve, increasing or decreasing the engine speed. The governor, by means of flyball weights, maintains the desired speed of the engine as set by the speed control lever.

When the governor cannot maintain the speed, the engine speeds up and then slows down, a condition known as hunting. When this happens, have the governor repaired by the dealer serviceman.

DIESEL ENGINE SYSTEM

It is important to use clean fuel in a gasoline system, but it is much more important to use clean fuel in a diesel system. Water and dirt *must* be kept out of the diesel system.

Secure clean fuel, store it in a tank containing a drain cock for drawing off water and sediment, transfer fuel to the tractor with a hose and nozzle that is kept capped when not in use and allow fuel to settle several hours before withdrawing any to place in the tractor. These precautions should insure clean fuel for the tractor tank. Always leave the tractor tank full at night to exclude moisture laden air. The tractor system fuel filters should remove any normal amount of water and dirt in the fuel.

Follow the directions in the Operator's Manual very carefully in maintaining and servicing the diesel engine fuel system.

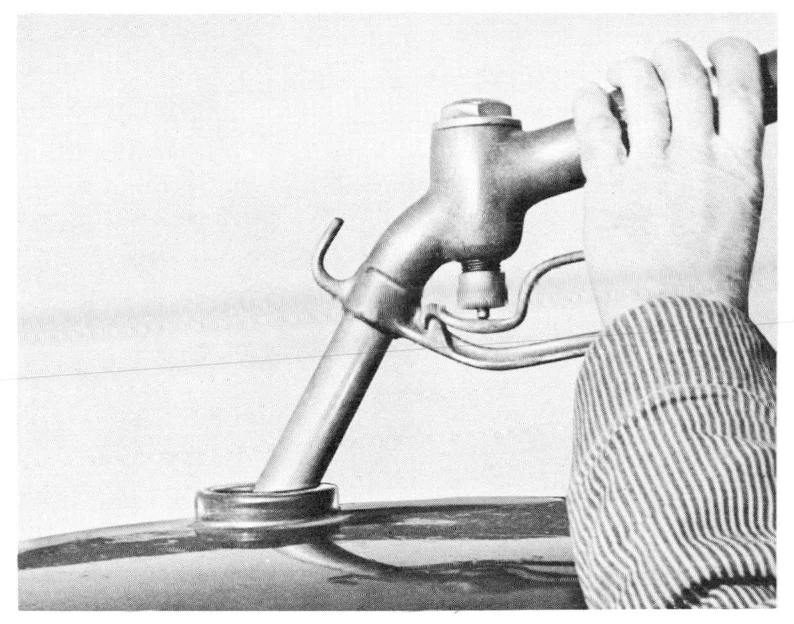

Courtesy International Harvester Co.

Fig. 9-7—Transfer fuel to the diesel tractor with a hose and nozzle that is kept capped when not in use.

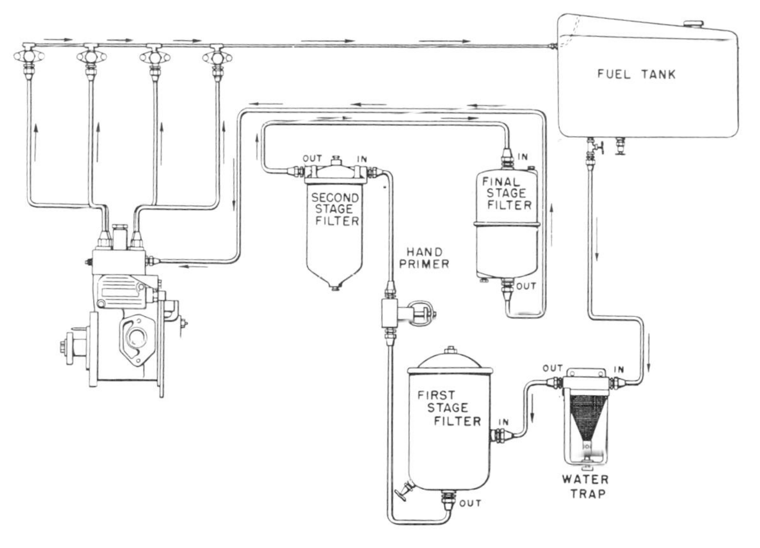

Courtesy Massey-Ferguson

Fig. 9-8—A diagram of a diesel fuel system. Note the filters.

Courtesy John Deere, Moline, Ill.

Fig. 9-9—Side view of a diesel tractor fuel system. Note the fuel pump, fuel filter with dual-stage element, injection pump and injectors to each cylinder.

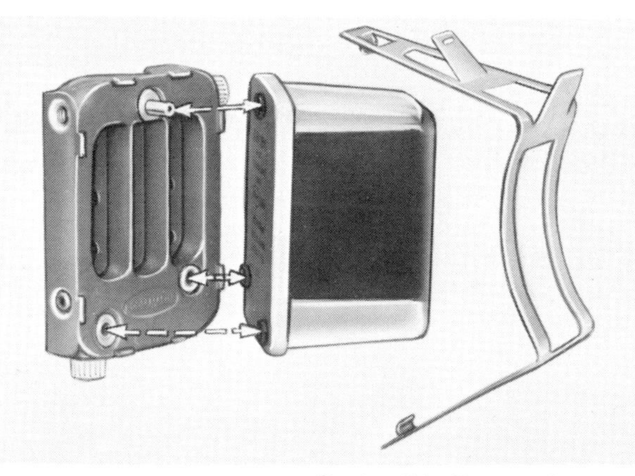

Courtesy John Deere, Moline, Ill.

Fig. 9-10—Dual-stage replaceable fuel filter element, filter body and filter retaining spring. Inspect the filter daily. If there is water or foreign matter at the bottom of the filter, loosen the filter drain plug at the bottom and drain the water and foreign matter. Bleed the filter after draining. The bleed plug is at the top of the filter body.

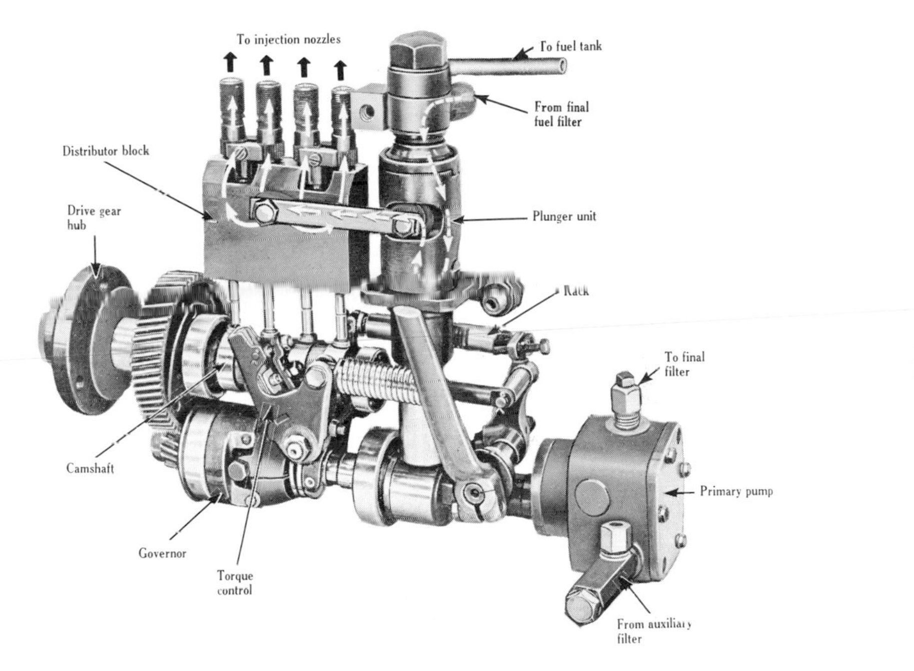

Courtesy International Harvester Co.

Fig. 9-11—The parts of a diesel injection system. Note the path of the fuel.

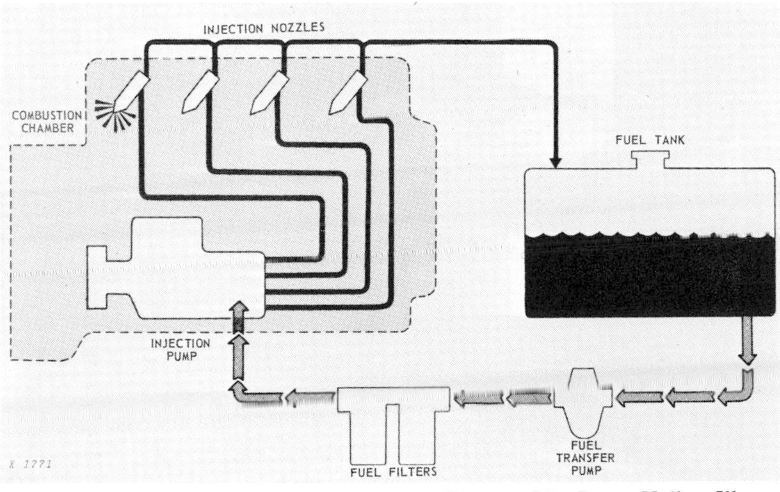

Courtesy John Deere, Moline, Ill.

Fig. 9-12—The parts of another diesel injection system.

Remember that you cannot be too careful in attempting to keep dirt and water out of the system.

Maintenance of the system will consist chiefly of servicing the filters. Service the sediment bowl or water trap daily or as often as water or sediment accumulates in the bowl. This should protect the rest of the filters in the system. Service the second and third stage filters as recommended by the manufacturer.

Any servicing or adjustment on the injectors should be done by the dealer serviceman. The operator should ordinarily keep

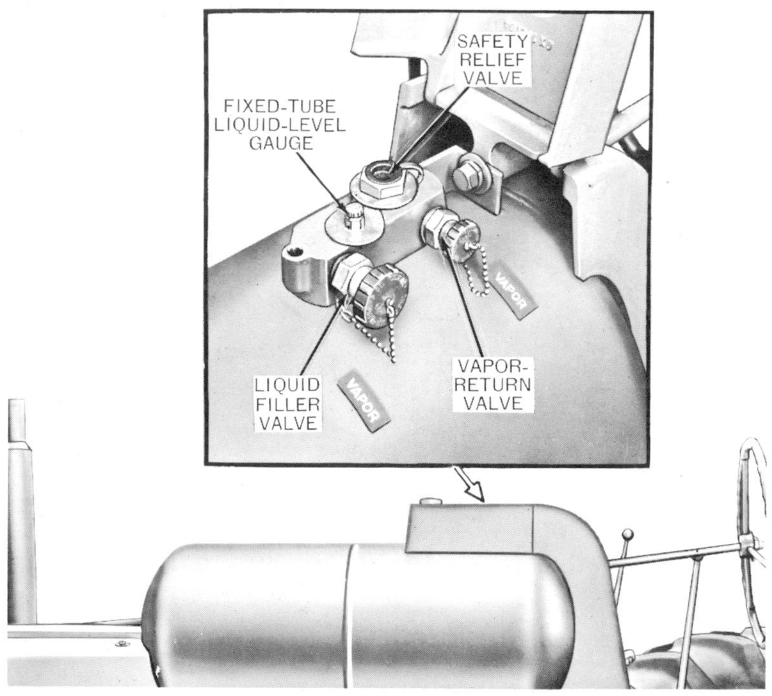

Courtesy John Deere, Moline, Ill.

Fig. 9-13—The fuel tank and filling devices on one LP gas tank. Note the liquid level gauge, the filter valve and vapor-return valve.

his hands off this part of the system because of the need for special equipment and special training.

LP GAS SYSTEM

The maintenance of the LP gas system is relatively simple in that the fuel is handled as a liquid under pressure. If reasonable care is used in keeping transfer hoses and fittings clean, there is very little chance for dirt to enter the system.

Read and follow the directions in the Operator's Manual in handling LP gas and operating the system. Service the filter as recommended.

Courtesy International Harvester Co.

Fig. 9-14—Never refuel the tractor while the engine is running or extremely hot.

QUESTIONS

1. Why is clean fuel so important in maintaining the fuel system?
2. Why is it recommended that diesel fuel be transferred from the storage tank to the tractor fuel tank through a hose rather than with containers and a funnel?
3. How does water get into a fuel tank?
4. Check in an Operator's Manual for the recommended interval for cleaning the fuel screen in the carburetor.
5. What damage can occur from a carburetor adjustment that is too lean?
6. What damage can occur from a carburetor adjustment that is too rich?
7. What three adjustments can usually be made on the carburetor of a tractor?
8. What should be done when the governor cannot maintain the engine at an even speed?
9. Why is clean diesel fuel so important?

CHAPTER 10

MAINTAINING THE IGNITION SYSTEM

The ignition system needs systematic servicing occasionally to bring about easy starting, quick warm-up and efficient operation of the tractor. Much of the servicing should be done by a competent serviceman with specialized equipment, usually at the time of the yearly tune-up. However, there are some important service jobs that the operator should do regularly.

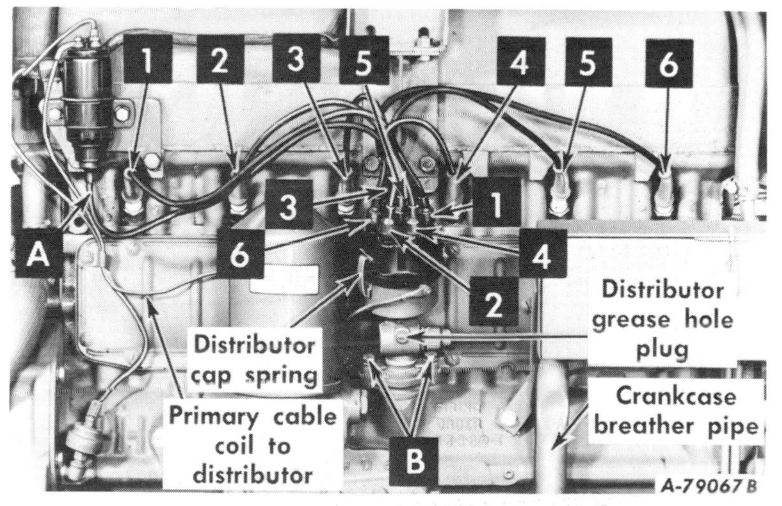

Courtesy International Harvester Co.

Fig. 10-1—A 6-cylinder tractor ignition system showing the coil, distributor and high tension leads to the spark plugs. Note the firing order on the block to the right and below the distributor.

BATTERY IGNITION SYSTEM

Battery ignition systems are taking the place of magneto systems on many tractors. The main difference between the two is the source of electric energy. In the battery system, the battery is the source, and in the magneto system, permanent magnets in the magneto set up a magnetic field independent of any other source of electric energy permitting the magneto to generate its own current when it is rotated.

Spark Plugs

Remove, clean and re-gap the spark plugs about every 250 hours of operation.

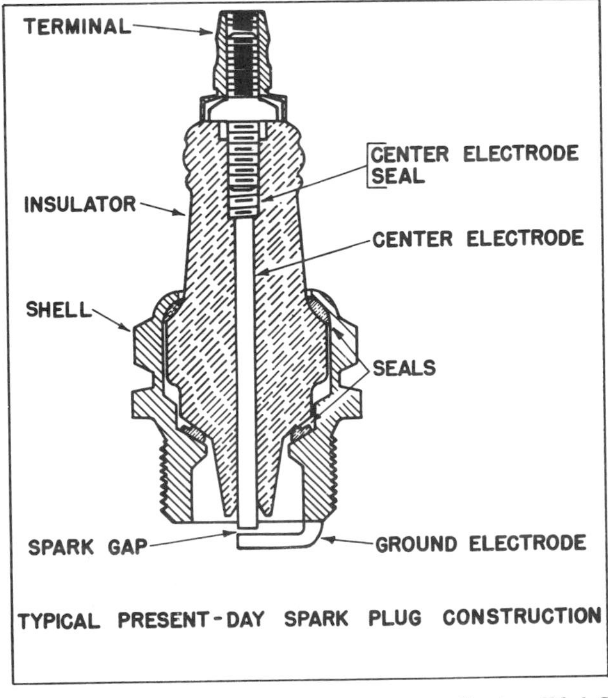

Courtesy Ethyl Corp.

Fig. 10-2—Typical present day spark plug construction.

Procedure

1. Brush or blow dirt from around the spark plug base.
2. Remove the plug with a wrench that fits the spark plug.
3. Examine the porcelain insulator and points. If the insulator appears to be melted or blistered, cracked or broken, and the points seem unduly burned, it is evident that the plug is operating too hot and should be replaced with a colder plug.

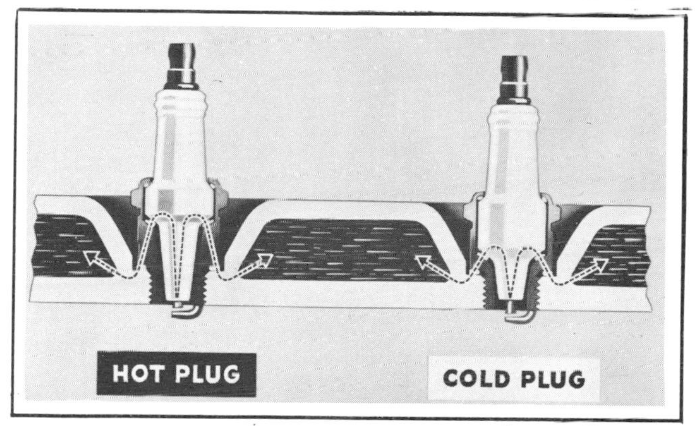

Courtesy Ethyl Corp.

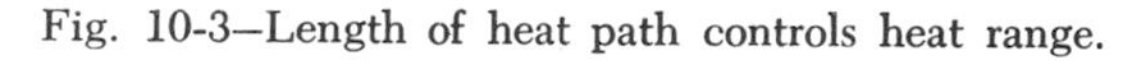

Fig. 10-3–Length of heat path controls heat range.

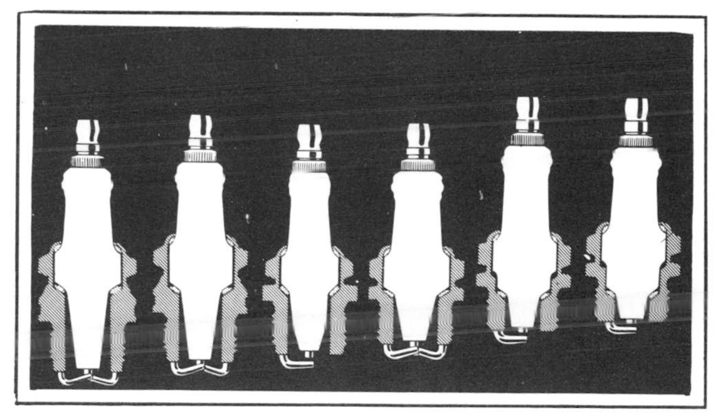

Courtesy Ethyl Corp.

Fig. 10-4–Insulator nose length and the location of the insulator in the shell determines length of heat path.

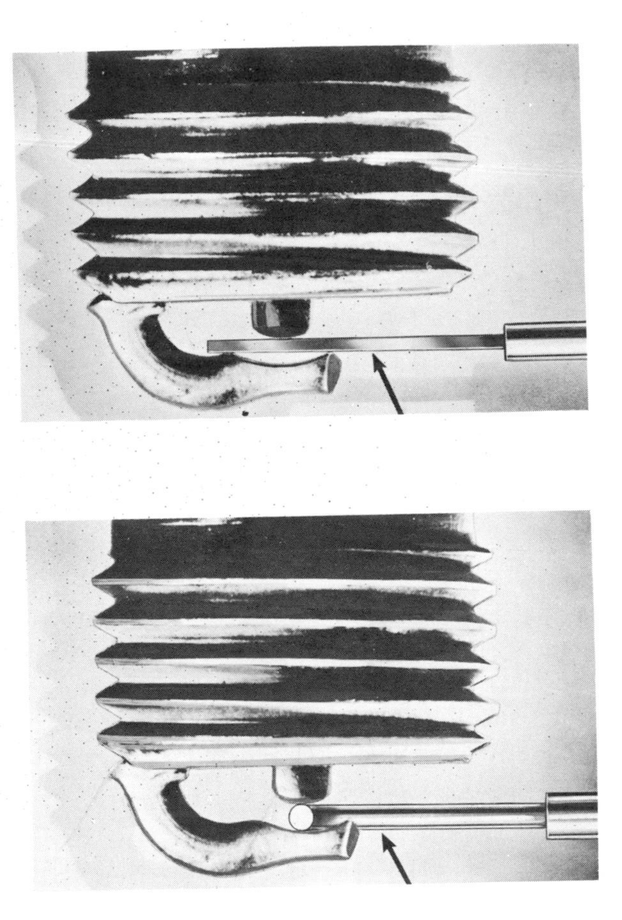

Courtesy Ethyl Corp.

Fig. 10-5—Round gap gauges insure correct settings.

If the plug is fouled excessively with carbon, it apparently is operating too cold and should be replaced with a hotter plug. Plug and engine manufacturers recommend specific plugs for specific uses. Even the correct style of plug will accumulate some carbon and the electrodes will scale to a certain extent. Carbon accumulation tends to allow leakage of electricity.

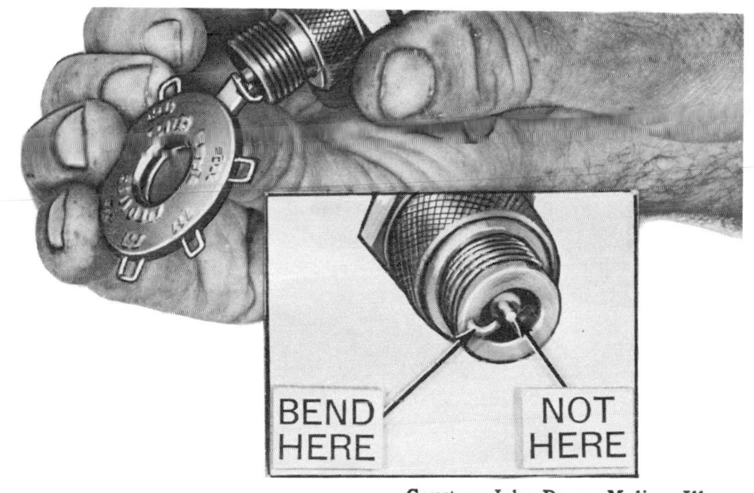

Courtesy John Deere, Moline, Ill.

Fig. 10-6—Setting spark plug point gap. Note the round gauge.

Corroded or scaled points tend to weaken the spark. A plug with a large gap may fire at low speeds but will not fire when the engine is under load at high speeds.

4. Misfit plugs should be replaced with the proper plugs.
5. Clean plugs in a sand-blast cleaner or with a wire brush.
6. Re-gap the plugs, using a round gauge and bend the outside electrode to the correct gap as recommended by the manufacturer. The gap will vary from 0.020 to 0.030 inches.
7. Replace the plugs, using a new gasket. Tighten the plugs with a torque wrench, to the recommended torque, usually about 30 foot pounds for the larger plugs.

Breaker Points

The breaker points should be checked about every 500 hours of operation. Continued use causes the points to pit and corrode so that the flow of current is obstructed and the strength of the spark is reduced. When the points are pitted badly, they should be replaced with good quality points by an experienced mechanic.

Don't try to save money by using off-brand replacement points. It is usually advisable to replace the condenser at the time points are replaced.

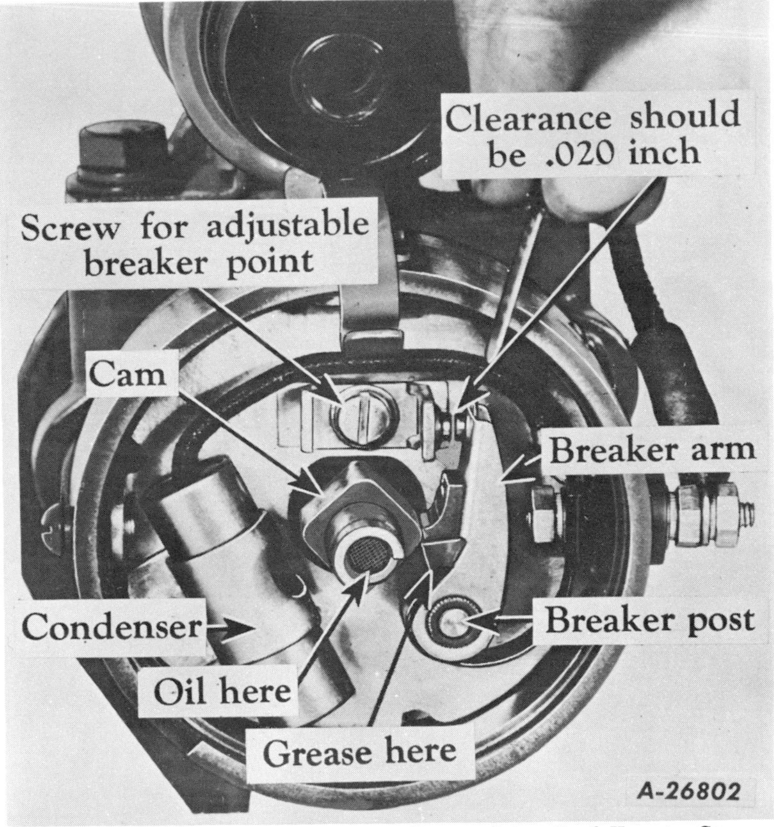

Courtesy International Harvester Co.

Fig. 10-7—Adjusting the breaker points. Check the Operator's Manual for clearance.

When the points need adjusting, proceed as follows:

Procedure

1. Remove and clean the ignition wires and distributor cap: inspect the cap for cracks.

2. Pull the distributor rotor from the shaft.
3. Remove the dust cap, if one is present.
4. Adjust the points.
   a. If there is a small tip on one point, it may be removed with a point file to give slightly longer service out of the points.

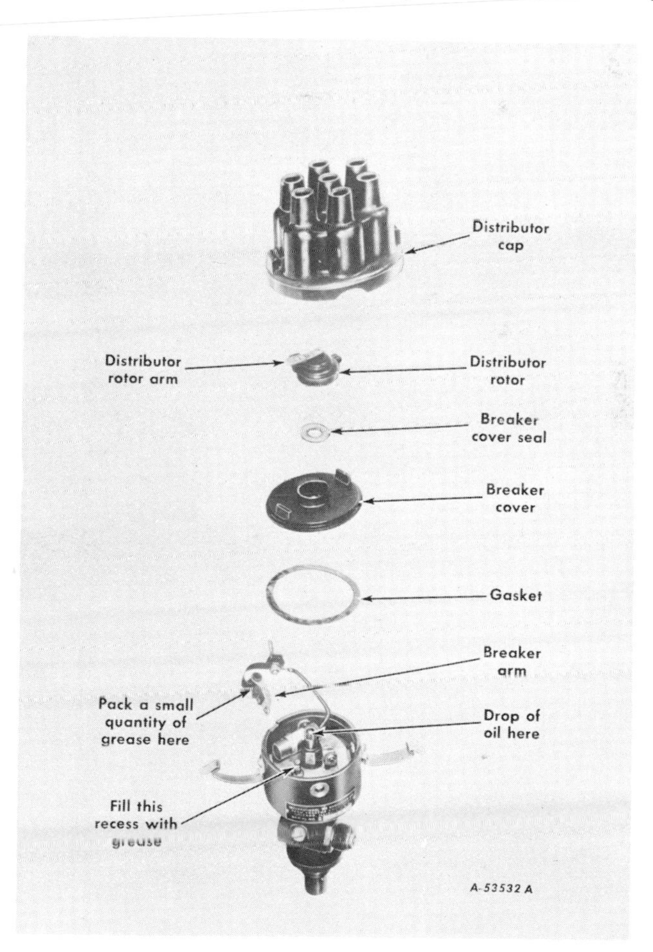

Courtesy International Harvester Co.

Fig. 10-8—Distributor partially disassembled for servicing.

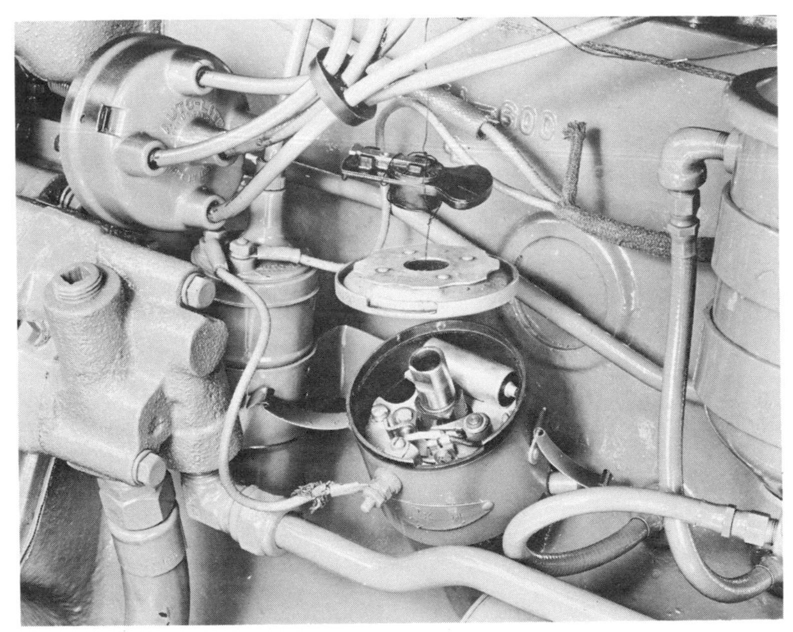

Courtesy Massey-Ferguson

Fig. 10-9—Note the dust cap and rotor on this distributor.

b. Crank the engine slowly until the points are open and the cam follower is on the peak of a lobe on the distributor cam.
c. Check the distance between the points with a clean feeler gauge. If the clearance is not right, move the movable point until the clearance is set according to the manufacturer's recommendation. Lock the adjustment.
d. Clean the points carefully with a clean cloth or paper towel to remove any grease or dirt that would cause early pitting.

5. Lubricate the distributor, following directions in the Operator's Manual.
   a. Place one drop of light oil on the breaker arm pivot pin.
   b. Place three to five drops of light oil in the felt wick in top of breaker cam.

c. Lubricate cam lobes very sparingly with hard grease. Do not overlubricate or get any grease on the points.

6. Replace the dust cap and distributor rotor.
7. Replace distributor cover and spark plug wires.

Coil

Hard starting, failure to start, irregular firing at high speeds, high fuel consumption and loss of power can result from a weak spark due to a faulty coil. Have the coil tested by a good ignition serviceman, and replace it if it is not up to standard.

Ignition Timing

When the distributor has been removed from the engine or the points have been adjusted, the timing will need to be checked. It is very important that the ignition be timed correctly for power, smooth operation and fuel economy.

Ignition timing is accomplished by placing No. 1 piston at top dead center of the compression stroke and adjusting the distributor so that the points open at this position, causing the spark which is distributed to No. 1 cylinder.

Two methods may be used to determine when No. 1 piston is on the compression stroke. (1) Remove the spark plug from No. 1 cylinder (usually the front cylinder), place your thumb over the spark plug hole; as the engine is cranked slowly by hand, a definite outward pressure will be felt as the piston comes up on the compression stroke. A slight pressure will be felt on the exhaust stroke; don't confuse the two strokes. (2) If the valve cover is off, the rocker arms and push rods on No. 1 cylinder will be free when the piston is on the compression stroke.

A top dead center mark (TDC) is usually on the flywheel or on the crankshaft pulley and will line up with a pointer when No. 1 piston is at top dead center. This mark will line up at top dead center on both the compression stroke and the exhaust stroke, so be sure of the compression stroke when timing.

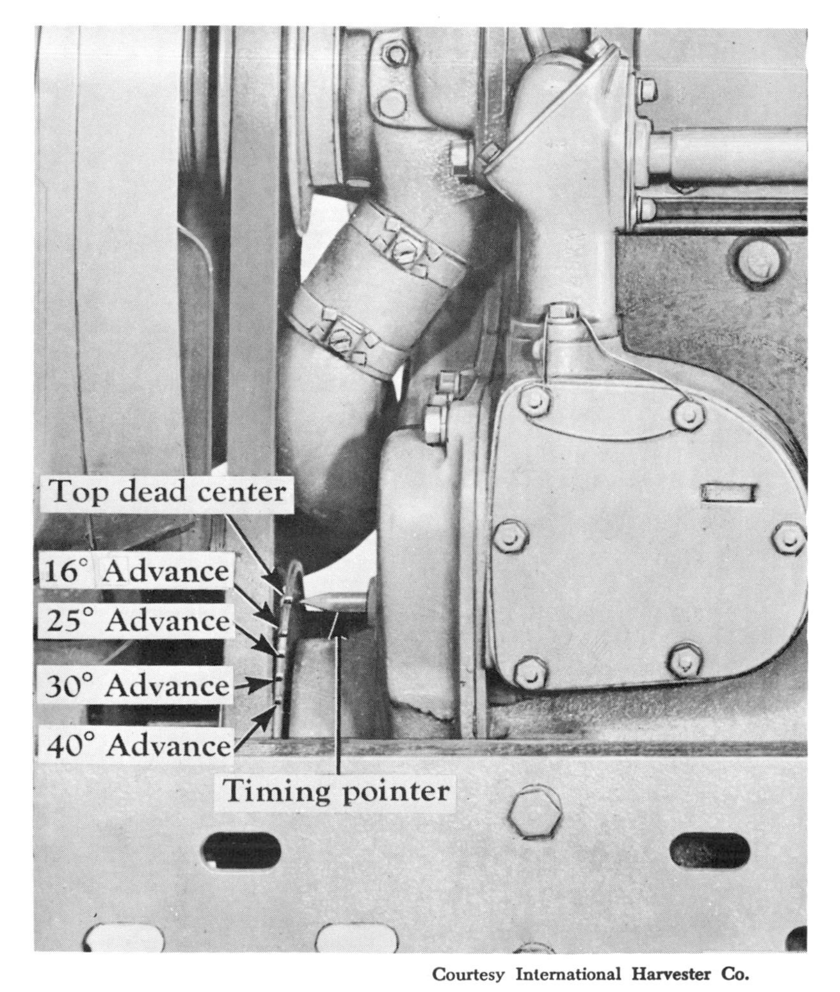

Courtesy International Harvester Co.

Fig. 10-10—Timing pointer and timing marks on one tractor.

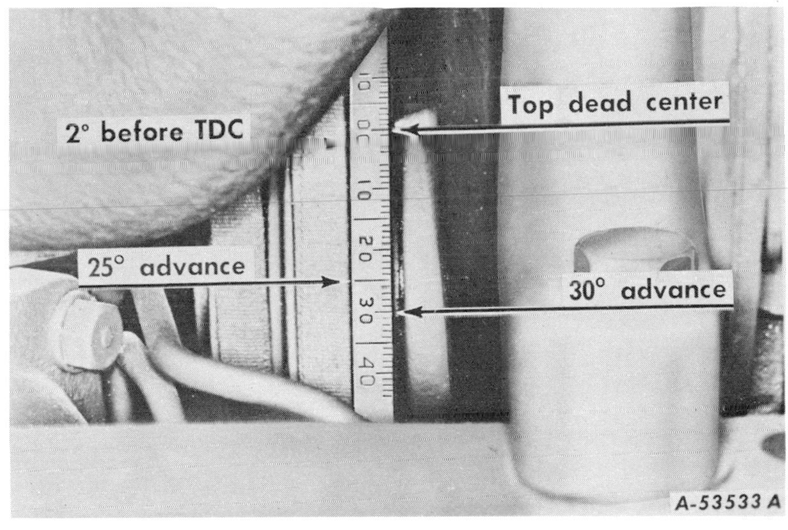

Courtesy International Harvester Co.

Fig. 10-11—Timing pointer and timing marks on the fan-drive pulley.

Procedure for CHECKING Ignition Timing

1. For safety, remove spark plug wires from the spark plugs.
2. Move No. 1 piston to near top dead center on the compression stroke by hand cranking the engine.
3. Turn the ignition switch on.
4. Hold No. 1 spark plug wire or the high voltage lead from the coil, near some part of the engine.
5. Continue cranking very slowly until a spark occurs.
6. Stop cranking and observe the location of the top dead center mark. It should be lined up exactly with the pointer. If it is not, an adjustment must be made by rotating the distributor until the spark does occur at top dead center.

Procedure for ADJUSTING the Ignition Timing

1. For safety, remove all spark plug wires from the spark plugs.
2. Move No. 1 piston to top dead center on the compression stroke.

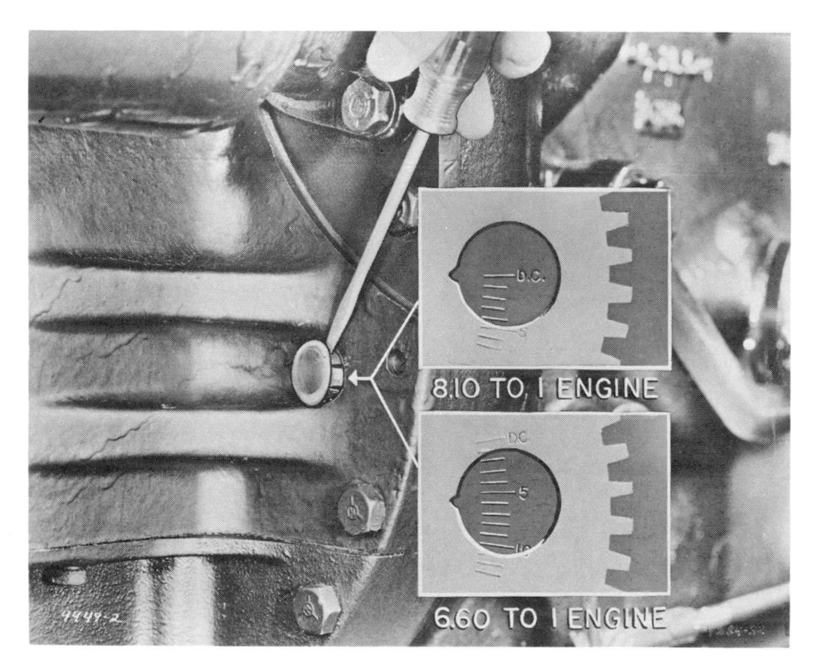

Courtesy Massey-Ferguson

Fig. 10-12—Timing marks on the flywheel and notch on inspection hole.

3. Loosen the distributor clamp until the distributor can be just moved by hand.
4. Turn the ignition switch on.
5. Rotate the distributor enough to close the points.
6. Have someone hold No. 1 spark plug wire or the high voltage lead from the coil, near some part of the engine.
7. Rotate the distributor slowly until the spark occurs when the points start to open.
8. Clamp the distributor in this position. The timing should be correct now, but it isn't always possible to get the distributor clamped without disturbing the adjustment.
9. Check the ignition timing.
   a. Rotate the crankshaft almost two revolutions until No. 1 piston is coming up on the compression stroke again.

Courtesy International Harvester Co.

Fig. 10-13—Showing the secondary cable held under the distributor cap spring for making a check on the timing.

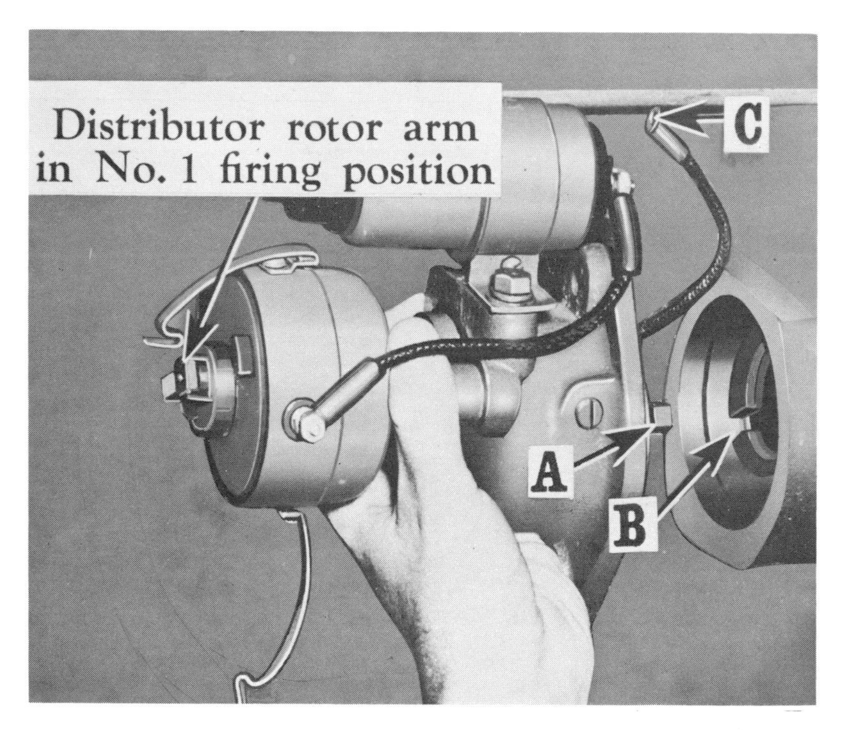

Courtesy International Harvester Co.

Fig. 10-14—Assembling the battery ignition unit. Note that the coil is included in this unit. The engine is now in firing position.

Courtesy International Harvester Co.

Fig. 10-15–Advancing the distributor while holding the secondary cable 1/16 to 1/8 inch from primary terminal.

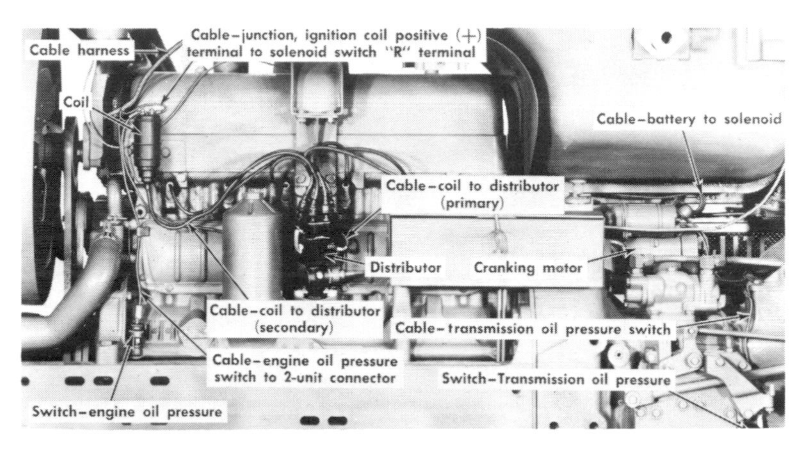

Courtesy International Harvester Co.

Fig. 10-16—Spark plug wiring. The engine firing order is 1, 5, 3, 6, 2, 4.

b. Hold the No. 1 spark plug wire as before.
c. Crank very slowly until a spark occurs, then stop cranking.
d. Check the top dead center mark. It should be lined up exactly with the pointer. If it is, the timing is correct. If it is not lined up, re-time the distributor until it is correct.

Timing Light

A timing light using a neon tube gives a quick, accurate way of checking or adjusting the ignition timing. The instructions for the proper hook-up and operation of the timing light, furnished by the manufacturer of the light, must be followed. Do not use a light designed for a 6 volt system only, on a 12 volt system or the light may be damaged.

When the light is properly connected to a power source and to the No. 1 spark plug cable, the light will flash as No. 1 spark plug is fired with the engine running. The light is directed on the timing marks and will show the relative position of the marks and the pointer at the time the spark occurs. The distributor can be rotated with the engine running until the timing is correct.

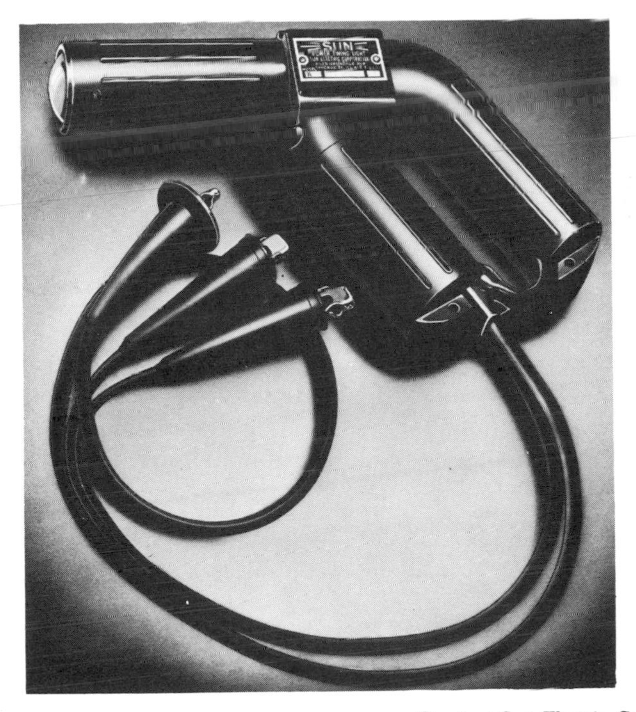

Courtesy Sun Electric Corp.

Fig. 10-17—A timing light.

It is extremely important to follow the instructions in the Operator's Manual accurately when timing the distributor with a timing light because most late model tractors are timed at a fast idle speed of 1900 to 2500 RPM. The spark advance at this speed is usually 19 to 20° before top dead center.

There may be several timing marks on the flywheel or pulley; the Operator's Manual will identify these marks. It is a good practice to whiten the marks with chalk or white paint before using the light, so they can be seen easily.

Courtesy John Deere, Moline, Ill.

Fig. 10-18—Final check of timing using power timing light. Follow directions in the manual for using the light.

MAGNETO IGNITION SYSTEM

Tractors equipped with a magneto ignition system will have the high tension (high voltage) type. These magnetos require some care to function well. Lubrication is necessary and the points must be serviced and maintained. If the magneto is loosened on the mounting pads or removed, re-timing will be necessary.

Any servicing of the magneto other than lubrication, cleaning, and point adjustment should be done by an experienced magneto serviceman with special magneto test equipment. It is a good practice to have the magneto checked once a year, at the time of the annual tuneup, by a good serviceman.

Procedure

1. Clean the magneto.

a. Keep dust and dirt from accumulating on the outside of the magneto.
b. Keep small ventilator holes open to prevent condensation in the magneto.

Courtesy American Oil Co.

Fig. 10-19—Remove dirt from the engine and ignition system. Dirt causes hard starting in damp weather.

2. Lubricate the magneto.
   a. Check the Operator's Manual for lubrication points on the magneto and follow directions carefully. Use the right kind and the right quantity of lubricant. Overlubrication is probably more common than underlubrication.
3. Lubricate the impulse coupling, if provision is made for its lubrication. The impulse coupling retards the spark when the engine is being cranked or running very slowly and flips the rotor forward rapidly for a part of a revolution to produce a hot spark for starting. If the impulse coupling isn't working, there is danger of the engine kicking back, because the spark

will occur before top dead center when the engine is cranked and the spark will be so weak it will be difficult to start the engine.

4. Service the breaker points.
   a. Check the point gap. Set the gap to the clearance recommended in the Operator's Manual, using a feeler gauge. If one point has a projection on it, the points will need to be dressed with a point file before the gauge can be used accurately. Badly pitted points should be replaced and the condenser checked. A faulty condenser or poor electrical connection between the condenser and the points will cause arcing and rapid burning of the points.
   b. Clean the breaker assembly.
5. Check the timing, using the procedure in the Operator's Manual because of differences in magnetos and timing procedure. In the absence of specific instructions, the following procedure will usually work:
   a. For safety, pull the high tension lead from the coil or from the center of the distributor cap.
   b. Locate the timing marks and pointer.
   c. Crank the engine slowly until top dead center of No. 1 cylinder is reached on the compression stroke; at this time the impulse coupling should trip. If the timing marks and pointer are lined up, the timing is correct.
6. The timing may be adjusted by loosening the magneto slightly and shifting it until the impulse trips just as the marks line up with the pointer.

QUESTIONS

1. What maintenance of the ignition system should be done by the tractor operator?
2. What is the difference between a "hot" spark plug and a "cold" spark plug?
3. Why should a new gasket be used when replacing spark plugs?

4. Why should a round gap gauge be used when checking the gap of used spark plugs?
5. Why should a torque wrench be used when installing spark plugs?
6. Approximately what torque should be used to install most spark plugs?
7. What effect does breaker point gap clearance have on ignition timing?
8. Which should be adjusted first, the breaker point gap clearance or the timing of the ignition?
9. How can you determine when No. 1 piston is approaching TDC on the compression stroke?
10. When checking the ignition timing, why can the high tension cable from the coil be used rather than the No. 1 spark plug cable?
11. What maintenance is usually needed on a magneto ignition system?
12. What is the purpose of the impulse coupling on a magneto?

CHAPTER 11

MAINTAINING THE ELECTRICAL SYSTEM

Most modern tractors are equipped with a complete electrical system—battery, starter, generator, voltage regulator, lights, switches and ammeter.

The major parts of the electrical system will require only minor service such as cleaning and lubrication. Major repairs will need to be done by a qualified electrical serviceman with test equipment.

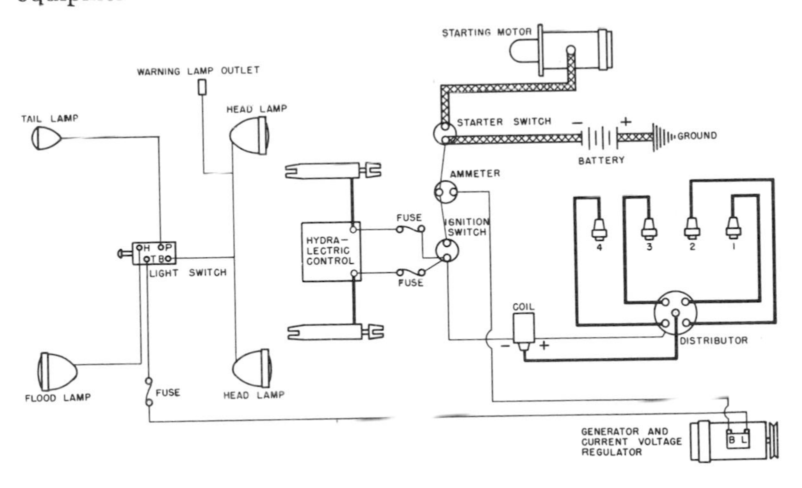

Courtesy Oliver Corp.

Fig. 11-1—Schematic wiring diagram

There are several maintenance jobs, however, that are the responsibility of the operator and must be done by him, regularly, to keep the system working. The most important of these jobs is servicing the battery.

Battery

1. Add pure water (distilled, if possible) as often as needed to keep the separators covered. Check at least once a week.
2. Take a battery hydrometer reading each week, before adding water. The reading for each cell should be between 1.250 and 1.275.
3. **Keep the battery fully charged at all times.**

Courtesy American Oil Co.

Fig. 11-2—For easy starting the battery should be in a fully charged condition. The condition of a battery can be checked with a battery hydrometer. Hold the hydrometer in a vertical position.

4. In cold weather, protect the battery from freezing by keeping it fully charged or stored in a cool place where the temperature will not drop below freezing.
5. Wipe the outside of the battery clean at least once a month with a damp cloth. If the terminals are corroded, brush them clean and apply a solution of baking soda, then flush the battery top with clean water. Coat the terminals with vaseline.

6. Do not permit the battery to bounce around in its carrier. Keep the battery hold-down bracket tightened enough to secure the battery, but not tight enough to damage the case.
7. Replace the battery when it will not hold a charge.

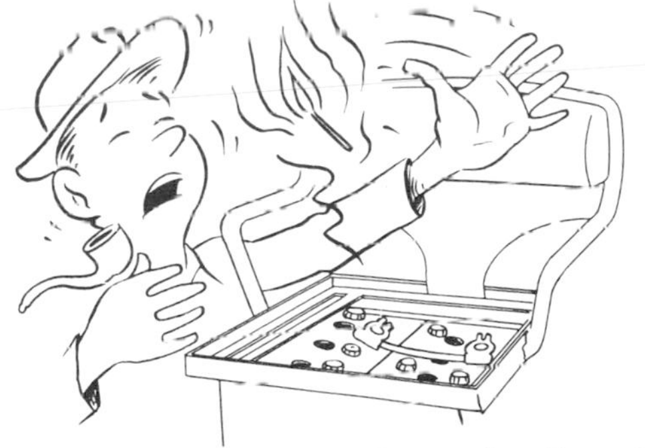

Courtesy John Deere, Moline, Ill.

Fig. 11-3–Keep flame away from battery filler cup opening.

Courtesy American Oil Co.

Fig. 11-4–Battery gas is highly explosive. Removing a wire while charging caused this battery to explode. Battery acid is dangerous.

8. Keep sparks or open flame away from the battery because the gas in the battery is highly explosive.

9. Keep battery cables clean and tight. A loose connection will prevent the battery from delivering the power necessary to crank the engine.

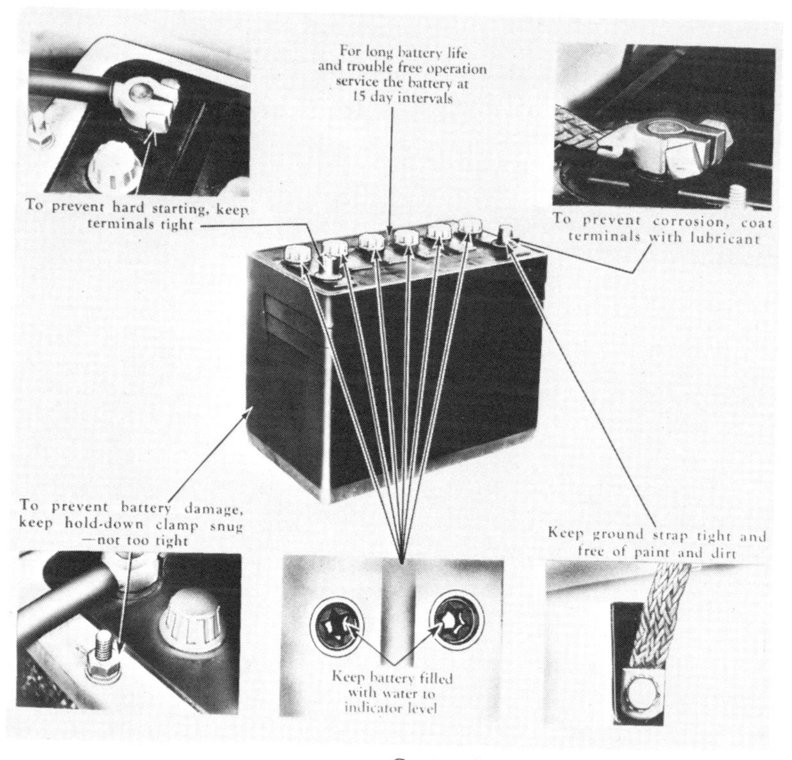

Courtesy International Harvester Co.

Fig. 11-5–Check points for maintaining the battery.

The specific gravity of the electrolyte indicates the relative condition of the battery charge and warns when it may be necessary to recharge the battery.

Inspect the battery once every two weeks to maintain the correct specific gravity. The specific gravity of a fully charged battery is 1.255 to 1.270 corrected to +80° F. (liquid temperature). A specific gravity reading of at least 1.230 corrected to +80° F. should be maintained. Never allow the battery to fall below 1.230.

The specific gravity reading will vary with the temperature of the electrolyte. For readings taken at any temperature other than +80° F., a temperature correction must be applied. This is done by adding .004 specific gravity for every 10° above +80° F., and by subtracting .004 specific gravity for every 10° below +80° F.

Example No. 1

Hydrometer reading 1.270
Electrolyte temperature ....+20° F.
Subtract .024 Sp. Gr. ....(.004 × 6)
Corrected Sp. Gr. is 1.246

Example No. 2

Hydrometer reading 1.255
Electrolyte temperature ....+100° F.
Add .008 Sp. Gr. ....(.004 × 2)
Corrected Sp. Gr. is 1.263

Courtesy International Harvester Co.

Generator

The generator will require lubrication occasionally, but care should be used not to overlubricate. Follow the directions in the Operator's Manual.

Keep the generator wiped clean.

When the commutator is dirty or slightly grooved, it may be cleaned by holding very fine sandpaper against it while the engine is running. Blow out any dust before replacing the cover strap.

Courtesy John Deere, Moline, Ill.

Fig. 11-6—Oil cups for lubricating the generator. Oil sparingly according to directions in Operator's Manual.

Replace generator brushes before they wear down too short and permit the generator to become damaged. It costs less to replace the brushes than it does to replace the generator and voltage regulator.

Alternator

Many tractors are equipped with an alternator rather than a generator. Alternators are generally more compact than generators and can supply a higher current at lower engine speeds.

Courtesy John Deere, Moline, Ill.

Fig. 11-7—A typical alternator installation. Note the size and shape of the alternator.

Basically the alternator is an a.c. generator in which the a.c. current is rectified to d.c. current electronically by the use of diodes. Usually alternators need no regular maintenance other than belt tension adjustment. Sealed bearings are used so no further lubrication is necessary. Certain safety rules must be followed, however, to prevent damage to the alternator charging circuit.

1. Disconnect the battery ground strap before working on the alternator or regulator.
2. NEVER POLARIZE THE ALTERNATOR. It is a recommended practice after any service work on a generator to polarize it by momentarily touching a jumper wire between the battery (B) and generator (G) terminals on the outside of the voltage regulator. THIS MUST NOT BE DONE if the engine is equipped with an alternator.

3. Always connect booster batteries POSITIVE to POSITIVE and NEGATIVE to NEGATIVE. Don't use a battery charger as a booster to aid in starting an engine equipped with an alternator.
4. Never disconnect or connect any alternator or regulator wiring with the alternator operating or with the batteries connected.

Courtesy International Harvester Co.

Fig. 11-8—The charge indicator will show the condition of the electrical system.

5. Never disconnect the batteries when the engine is running and the alternator is charging.

   NOTE: Any sudden or excessive surge of current through the alternator charging circuit can severely damage the diodes in the alternator.

Starter

The starter will give long service if cleaned occasionally and lubricated correctly. Keep electrical connections clean and tight.

Courtesy International Harvester Co.

Fig. 11-9—Cleaning the cranking motor commutator with No. 00 sandpaper. Blow dust out after cleaning.

QUESTIONS

1. What maintenance jobs on the electrical system should be done by the tractor operator?
2. What regular maintenance does the battery require?
3. How can the battery be protected from freezing?
4. Why should the battery be secured so that it cannot bounce around in the battery carrier?
5. Why should flames and sparks be kept away from the battery openings?
6. Why should the generator be oiled sparingly?
7. What effect does the temperature of the electrolyte have on the specific gravity reading?
8. Why is it important to keep the liquid level up in a battery?
9. What are the differences between an alternator and a generator?
10. Why should a generator be polarized after any service work is done on it?
11. Why is it important to never polarize an alternator?

CHAPTER 12

MAINTAINING THE HYDRAULIC SYSTEM

The hydraulic system of a modern tractor enables the operator to operate mounted or pull-type implements quickly and easily. With a weight transfer attachment, the hydraulic system aids in improving traction by transferring weight from trailing implements and the front of the tractor to the drive wheels.

Power steering, power brakes and power shifting are parts of the hydraulic system on some tractors. Other devices in the hydraulic system are two or more pumps, one or more hydraulic oil filters, an oil cooler, control valves, an accumulator and hydraulic cylinders with hoses, pipes or tubes and couplings.

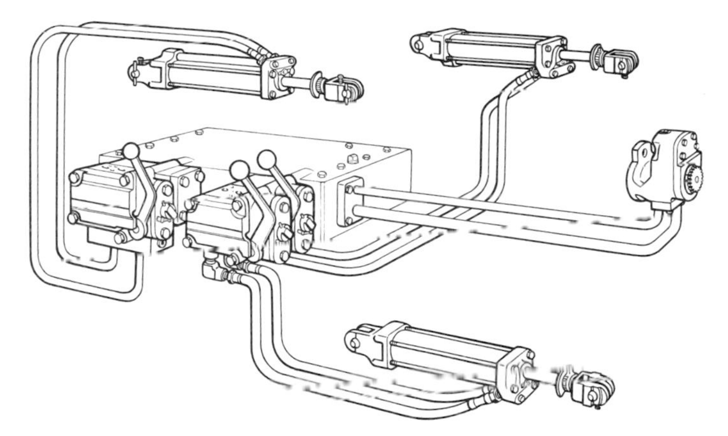

Courtesy International Harvester Co.

Fig. 12-1—One hydraulic system with three cylinders for rear tractor-mounted, trailing-type, and right and left front tractor mounted implements.

The operator should read the instructions in the Operator's Manual and follow them carefully. There are many differences in the design and operation of hydraulic systems on different makes of tractors. Improper operation and servicing can cause premature damage and failure of seals and other parts.

Practically all late model tractors have a transmission-hydraulic system with the power train lubricated with hydraulic oil rather than the gear oil used in older model tractors. In the new tractors, the transmission, differential and final drive operate in a bath of hydraulic oil.

The maintenance of the hydraulic system is very similar for older tractors with a separate hydraulic system and late models with a transmission-hydraulic system.

MAINTENANCE

1. Change the hydraulic oil filter after the first 10 hours and first 100 hours in a new tractor.
2. Change the hydraulic oil filter at the recommended intervals after the first 100 hours of operation.
3. Check the hydraulic oil level periodically, at least every 200 hours, after the tractor is broken in.
4. Drain and refill the hydraulic system at the intervals recommended by the manufacturer.
5. Do everything possible to keep dust and dirt out of the system. Dirt is the worst enemy of the hydraulic system because of the damage it can do to pump parts and seals.
6. Take care to keep couplings clean when connecting remote cylinders.
7. Keep dust caps and dust plugs on all hydraulic cylinder couplings to help protect them from dirt and grit when couplings are disconnected.
8. Keep hydraulic oil containers absolutely clean, and use extreme care when adding oil or refilling so that no dirt can get into the system from around the filter cap, funnels or from dust in the air.

Courtesy John Deere, Moline, Ill.

Fig. 12-2—Pump pistons scored by contaminated fluid.

9. Keep the hydraulic oil cooler clean to help prevent overheating of the hydraulic oil. If the hydraulic oil has been overheated, check with the tractor dealer. It may be advisable to drain and refill the system with new hydraulic oil and change the filter.
10. Operate the hydraulic units on the tractor correctly and carefully.
11. Always use the hydraulic oil recommended by the manufacturer. The wrong oil in the system can damage seals and lead to premature failure of parts of the hydraulic system.

Hydraulic Oil

The experience of tractor manufacturers indicates that most hydraulic problems come about because of the use of the wrong hydraulic oil or the use of one containing dirt and other contaminants.

It is extremely important to use the hydraulic oil recommended by the manufacturer. Most systems are designed to use a highly refined petroleum oil containing specific additives.

The hydraulic oil must transmit power, lubricate all moving parts, protect the metal parts of the system from rust and corrosion, resist oxidation and foaming and separate itself readily from air, water and other contaminants. The oil must also be stable over a long period of time and maintain the proper viscosity through a wide range of temperatures.

In order to have all these properties, various additives are incorporated into the oil. Viscosity index improver is added so that viscosity change over a wide range of temperatures is as little as practical.

An "extreme pressure" additive is often blended with the hydraulic oil for late model tractors when the hydraulic oil must lubricate the transmission, differential and final drive. This additive helps in the lubrication of close-fitting parts operating under high pressures and temperatures to prevent galling, scoring, seizure and wear.

An oxidation inhibitor is added to reduce the oxidation of the hydraulic oil as it is exposed to air in the system. Oxidation can form harmful contaminants, such as acids and sludge. Changing hydraulic filters regularly, changing hydraulic oil as recommended and keeping the oil cooler clean will assist in reducing oxidation and sludge formation in the system.

Rust and corrosion inhibitors are included to neutralize corrosion-forming acids and to cling to metal parts to protect them from rusting and corrosion. Rusting causes tight-fitting parts to become larger while corrosion tends to eat away the metal leaving rough spots which damage seals and releasing minute metal particles to circulate through the system to cause premature wear and failure.

Foam inhibitors help the hydraulic oil dissolve air bubbles and reduce foaming which can cause unsatisfactory operation and poor lubrication.

The additives in the hydraulic oil help hold contaminants in suspension and protect the system but will eventually lose their effectiveness after a certain period of time. The hydraulic oil must be drained while the contaminants are still in suspension and the additives are still protecting the system. The oil change interval recommended by the manufacturer indicates the maximum number of hours of operation that the hydraulic oil can be expected to maintain its ability to protect the system.

Operation

The hydraulic system can be hooked-up, on most tractors, to operate a variety of different implements. They may be front-mounted, rear-mounted or a combination of the two. The operator will need to consult the Operator's Manual in order to understand how to hook-up the system and set the controls for the different possible operations.

Courtesy John Deere, Moline, Ill.

Fig. 12-3—Never overload the hydraulic system.

The hydraulic pump on some older tractors with a separate hydraulic system can be disengaged when the system is not in use. On some late model tractors the hydraulic pump can be shut off as an aid to starting in cold weather.

On most tractors there is an adjustment for increasing or decreasing the speed of lifting or dropping implements. As a general rule, the heavier implements should be lifted more slowly to avoid undue strain on the system.

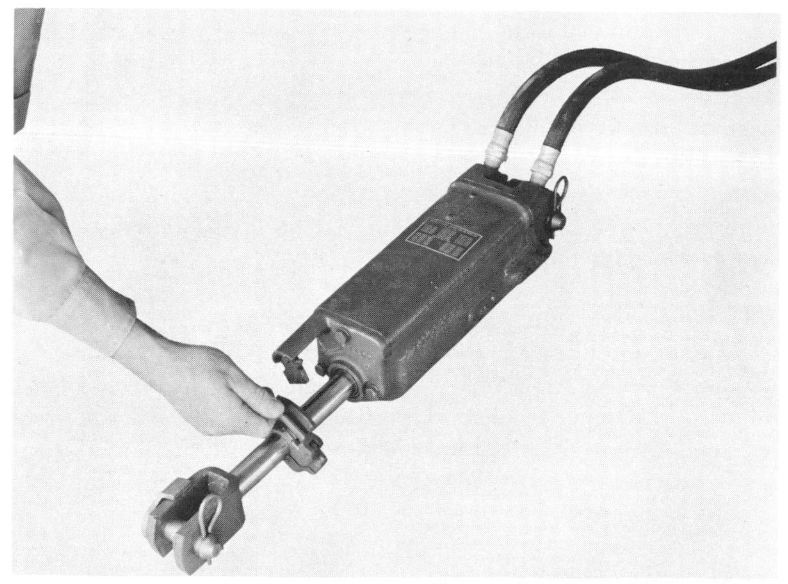

Courtesy John Deere, Moline, Ill.

Fig. 12-4—Double-acting hydraulic-stop-type remote cylinder. The stop lever is being adjusted.

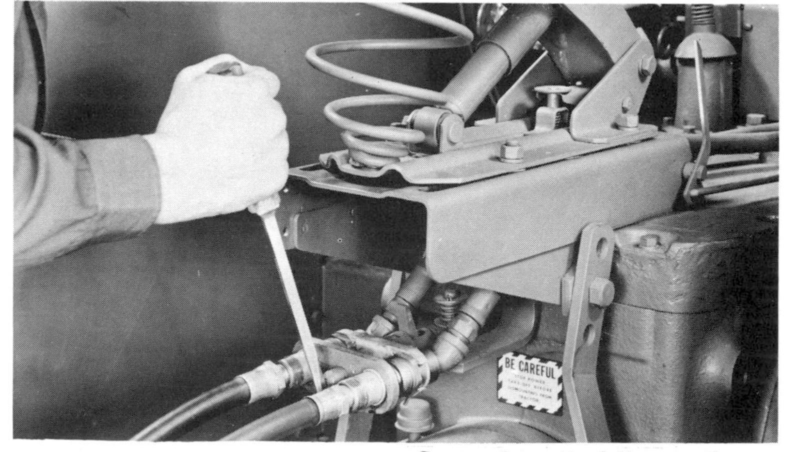

Courtesy International Harvester Co.

Fig. 12-5—Connecting the break-away coupling. Wipe the coupling clean before making the connection. Keep dust caps in place when the remote cylinder is not being used.

Courtesy International Harvester Co.

Fig. 12-6—Installing a remote cylinder on an implement. Is this cylinder single-acting or double-acting?

Courtesy International Harvester Co.

Fig. 12-7—Adjusting the stop lever to control length of stroke.

Never overload the system. Most implements have auxiliary springs to assist in lifting. These should be adjusted to take as much load off the system as possible.

Remote Cylinders

Remote cylinders may be single acting or double acting depending upon their construction and method of attachment. It is usually best to attach the cylinder to the implement so that the heaviest load is on the cylinder when it is extending, because more piston surface is exposed to the hydraulic pressure. Stops are provided on the piston rod to adjust the length of stroke to the requirements of the implement. Clamp the stop securely so it does not work and damage the piston rod.

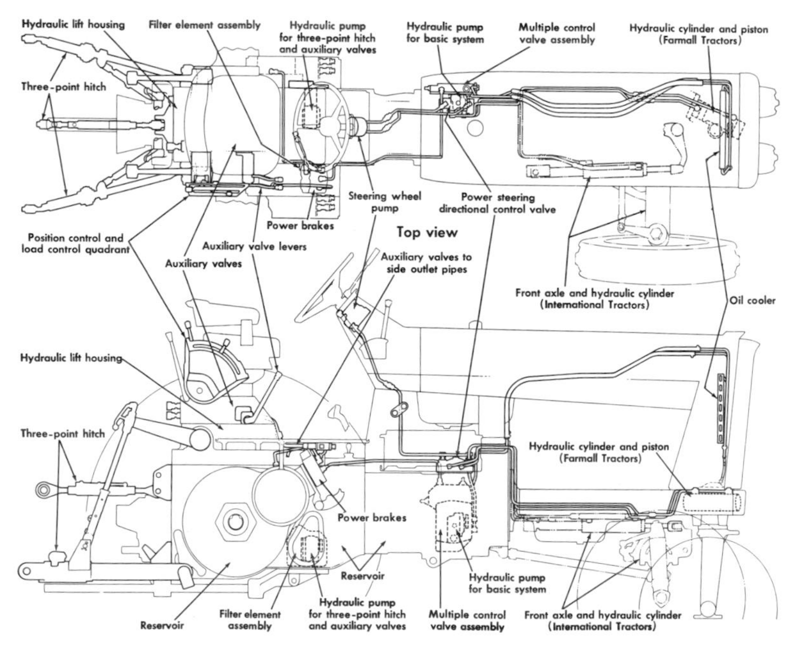

Courtesy International Harvester Co.

Fig. 12-8—The hydraulic system of a typical tractor. Note the location of the filter element. The transmission and final drive are lubricated by the hydraulic fluid.

Keep dust caps on lines and fittings when they are not connected. Most systems have break-a-way and quick-disconnect fittings to speed attachment, to conserve hydraulic fluid and to help keep out dirt. Some fluid will be present on the fittings and this fluid will collect dust. The fittings should always be wiped clean before hoses are attached.

Extra fluid will usually be needed in the system to replace that pumped into the cylinder when an empty remote cylinder is attached.

Maintaining Fluid Level

The proper fluid level should be maintained in the system to get the maximum extension and to prevent damage. The pump and valves are lubricated by the hydraulic system and can be damaged if the fluid gets low. Wipe the filler plug clean before removing it. Always use clean containers for hydraulic fluid. Canned oil is easier to keep clean, if the cans are wiped before opening.

Changing Filters

Even with careful maintenance some contaminants will accumulate in the hydraulic system. The filter or filters remove

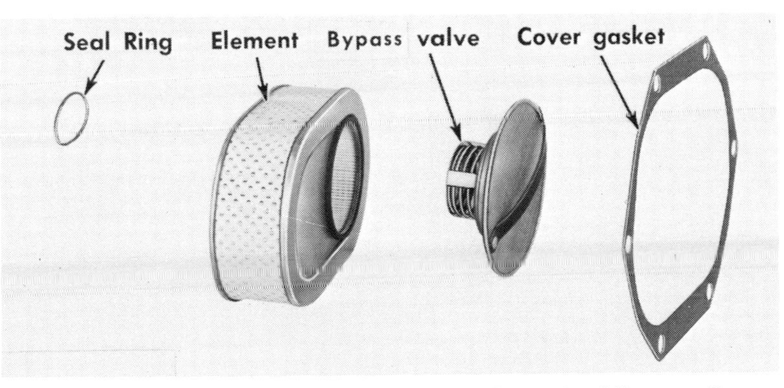

Courtesy International Harvester Co.

Fig. 12-9—Hydraulic system fluid filter disassembled.

contaminants as the oil circulates but the filter must be changed before it has absorbed all the dirt and contaminants it can hold and stops working. The filter change interval recommended by the manufacturer indicates the hours of operation the filter will protect the system under normal conditions. The filter should be changed more often under abnormally dusty conditions or high-temperature operation.

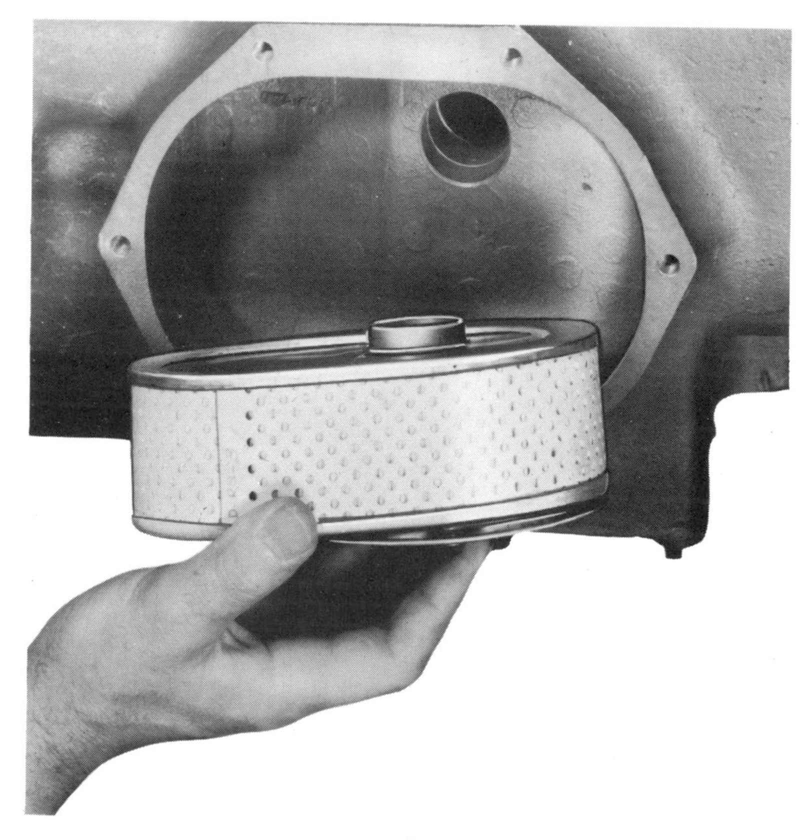

Courtesy International Harvester Co.

Fig. 12-10—Installing the hydraulic system filter.

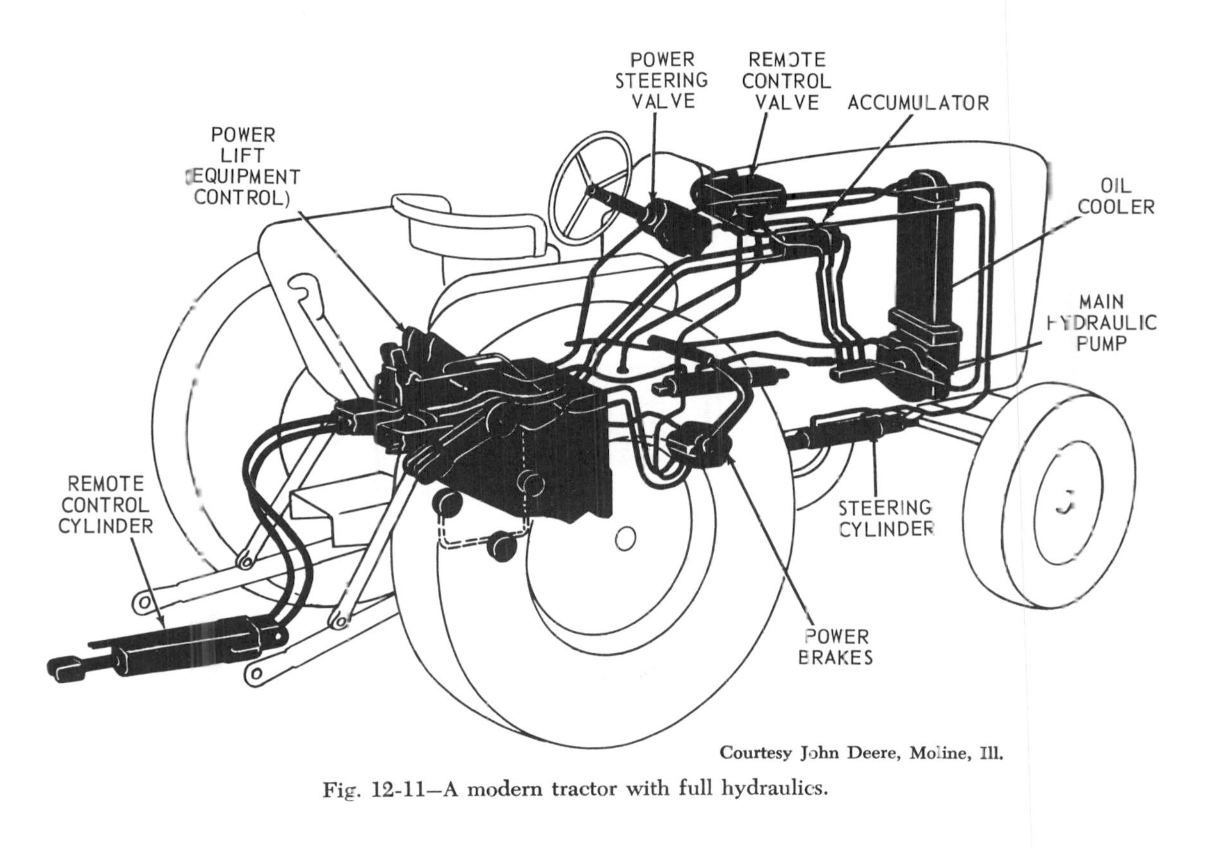

Courtesy John Deere, Moline, Ill.

Fig. 12-11—A modern tractor with full hydraulics.

Changing Hydraulic System Oil

Recommendations vary some between makes of tractor, but the hydraulic oil should usually be drained at least once a year. The hours of operation will vary from 600 to 1,000 or 1,200 hours with different manufacturers. Regular drainage of the entire hydraulic system is extremely important to remove products of oxidation, such as acids and sludge, water which tends to accumulate in the system, minute metal particles and other contaminants. Drain the system when the hydraulic oil is warm, and more of the contaminants will be removed.

Flushing

If the drained oil has sediment and sludge in it, the hydraulic system should be flushed before refilling. Follow the manufacturer's recommendation carefully, or have this done at the dealer's service department. Probably the only safe flushing agent to use is the hydraulic oil regularly used in the system. Change the filter,

Courtesy John Deere, Moline, Ill.

Fig. 12-12—Keep the oil clean.

and fill the system with the recommended hydraulic oil and operate the equipment to cycle the oil through the system until the hydraulic equipment operates satisfactorily. This may take several hours. Drain the flushing oil, replace the filter or filters and refill with the recommended hydraulic oil.

If the hydraulic equipment does not operate correctly, there are probably gum and lacquer deposits present, and the system will have to be taken apart and cleaned manually. This should probably be done by the tractor dealer service department and certainly only by a qualified mechanic. Regular draining and servicing of the hydraulic system should reduce the formation of gum and lacquer.

A magnetic drain plug is ordinarily used in hydraulic systems. The plug collects small particles of metal and keeps them from circulating in the system. The drain plug should be thoroughly cleaned before it is replaced.

QUESTIONS

1. Why should dirt be kept out of the hydraulic system?
2. Why is correct operation and servicing so important when working with the hydraulic system?
3. When should the adjustment be made to change the speed at which implements may be raised?
4. What damage may occur if the system is operated when the liquid level is low?
5. Why should the hydraulic system be drained and refilled at least once a year?
6. Check an Operator's Manual to see how often the hydraulic system filter should be changed.
7. What is the purpose of auxiliary lifting springs on some implements?

CHAPTER 13

MAINTAINING THE POWER TRANSMISSION SYSTEM

The power transmission system is made up of the clutch, transmission, differential and final drive.

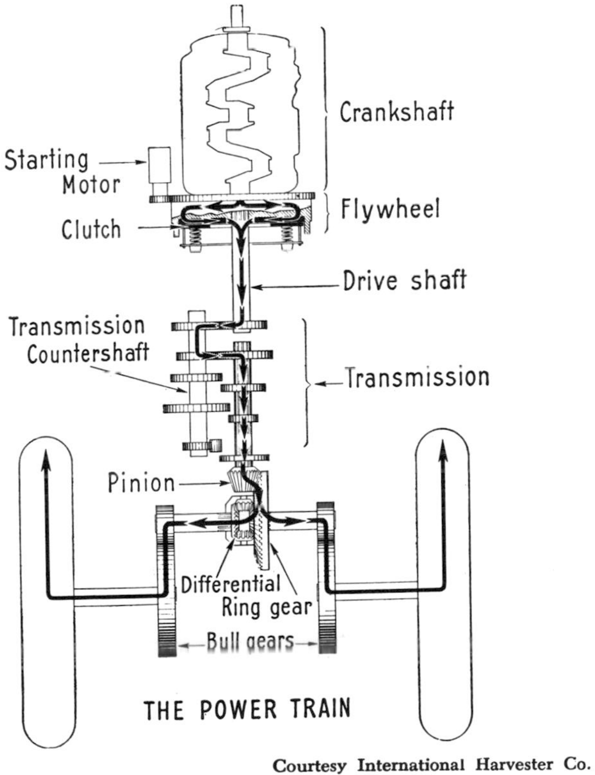

Courtesy International Harvester Co.

Fig. 13-1—The power transmission system.

Clutch

Clutch troubles are not unusual and are usually due to misuse or abuse, neglect, or to normal wear without proper adjustment. Correct lubrication is essential. Too much lubricant causes trouble and too little allows unnecessary wear and expense.

A common form of abuse is the habit of keeping the foot on the clutch pedal or "riding" the clutch. This causes the clutch to slip, heat and wear. Excessive slipping of the clutch by failing to engage it quickly will cause wear.

Courtesy Massey-Ferguson

Fig. 13-2—Don't "ride" the clutch pedal.

When difficulty is experienced in shifting gears without clashing, the clutch probably needs adjusting. Changes in the action of the clutch are so gradual it is often difficult for the operator to notice that an adjustment is needed unless he drives another tractor of the same make and age with a clutch that is in adjustment. Follow the instructions in the Operator's Manual in making this important adjustment. Adjust the clutch at the first sign of difficulty in shifting. A slipping clutch will burn out quickly.

There are few moving parts in a clutch, but these few parts require lubrication. Some are packed with grease and sealed and need lubrication only when the clutch is repaired. On some clutches, the throw out bearing is lubricated with a grease fitting

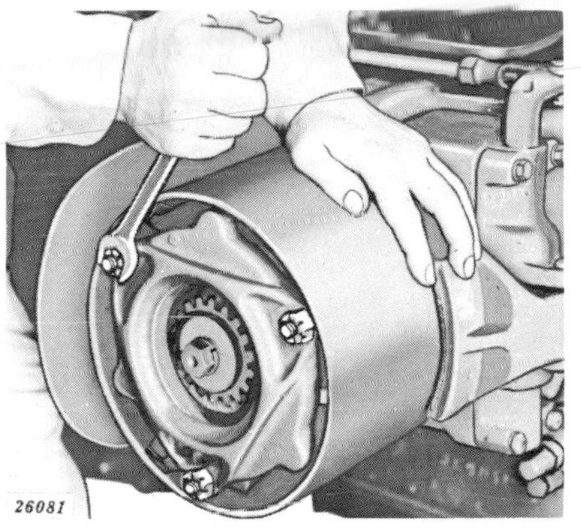

Courtesy John Deere, Moline, Ill.

Fig. 13-3—Adjusting the clutch.

which must be lined up with an opening in the clutch housing. The main precaution in lubricating this bearing is not to overlubricate. Excess grease will get on the clutch facing and cause slippage.

Transmission, Differential and Final Drive

The service necessary for these gear cases on older tractors without a combination transmission-hydraulic system is to maintain the lubricant level and drain, flush and refill at least once a year.

There is a tendency for the operator not to change the lubricant for several years because of the cost of the several gallons needed and because he has operated older tractors in this way without serious trouble. It is well to keep in mind that the modern tractor is more powerful than older tractors and requires better lubrication which is supplied by the modern extreme pressure transmission oil. This improved transmission oil contains additives to enable it to do the job and the additives cannot last indefinitely.

Courtesy John Deere, Moline, Ill.

Fig. 13-4–Removing transmission hydraulic system oil filter element.

The oil should be changed regularly in order to keep the gears and bearings supplied with good, clean lubricant. Contaminants such as fine dust, rust particles, moisture from condensation and small metal particles will accumulate and the only way to remove them is to drain the oil. Most manufacturers recommend changing the oil once a year or every 1000 hours. Under no circumstances should the oil be left in a modern tractor over three years.

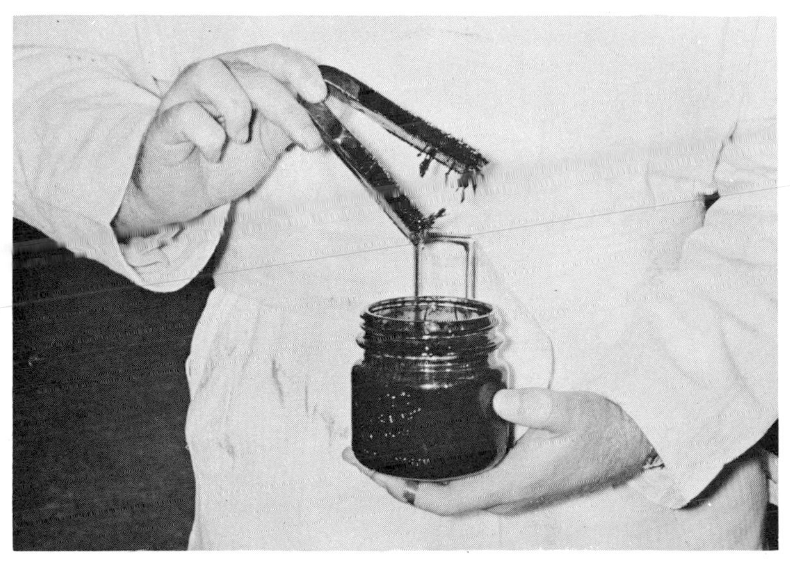

Courtesy American Oil Co.

Fig. 13-5—Magnetic material, gear teeth chips which have collected in the tractor transmission case.

Drain, Flush and Refill

Procedure

1. Have the tractor and gear cases thoroughly warmed up.
2. Drain the transmission, differential and final drive while still hot.
3. Replace drain plugs and fill with kerosene or furnace oil.
4. Either drive the tractor around a few minutes or jack up one rear wheel and run the tractor a few minutes in low gear.
5. Drain the flushing oil thoroughly.
6. Replace drain plugs and refill with the recommended weight of transmission oil.

The procedure just outlined applies to tractors using transmission lubricant in the gear cases.

In most modern tractors the transmission, differential and final drive are lubricated by the hydraulic fluid. Changing the hydraulic filter regularly and draining and refilling the hydraulic system with the recommended fluid should remove most of the contaminants and maintain the system in good condition.

Courtesy American Oil Co.

Fig. 13-6—Protect the tire when draining the final drive.

QUESTIONS

1. What major assemblies are included in the power transmission system?
2. What is the function of the clutch, the transmission, the differential and the final drive?
3. What is meant by the term "riding the clutch"?
4. Why should the clutch be engaged quickly?
5. What indicates the need for adjustment of the clutch?
6. Why is it more important to change the transmission oil regularly on a late model tractor than it is on a ten year old model?
7. Why should the transmission oil be changed?

CHAPTER 14

MAINTAINING THE CHASSIS

The chassis of the tractor may be considered to be that part of the tractor neither engine nor transmission. It includes the frame, wheels, brakes, steering mechanism and tires.

The maintenance of the chassis consists of regular lubrication and an occasional adjustment. Because of differences in design between makes of tractors, the Operator's Manual will need to be checked for specific procedures and for the periods when lubrication is needed.

Steering Gear

The steering mechanism usually needs little servicing other than thorough lubrication and an occasional adjustment. Neglect of the system, however, will cause unnecessary wear, hard steering and costly repairs.

Power steering is common on the larger tractors and is essentially a part of the hydraulic system. Most of the parts are lubricated by the hydraulic fluid and little adjustment is needed.

Procedure—Manual Steering

1. Check and refill gear housing at recommended intervals.
   a. Remove grill, if necessary, and housing cover or fill plug.
   b. Refill to recommended level with correct lubricant. Do not overfill as the excess will run out.
2. Check for play or backlash in the steering gears.
3. Adjust gears according to directions in the Operator's Manual. (This will be necessary only after several years use.)

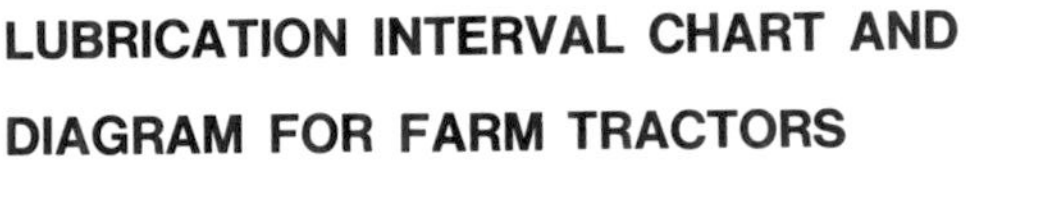

LUBRICATION INTERVAL CHART AND DIAGRAM FOR FARM TRACTORS

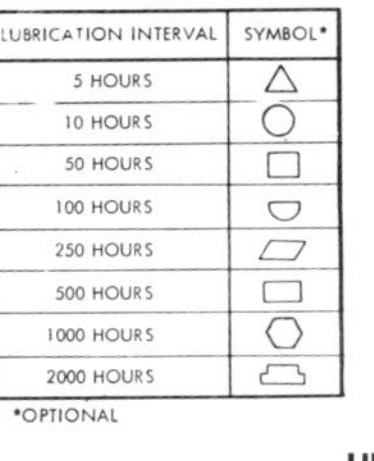

LUBRICATION INTERVAL	SYMBOL*
5 HOURS	△
10 HOURS	○
50 HOURS	□
100 HOURS	◡
250 HOURS	▱
500 HOURS	▭
1000 HOURS	⬡
2000 HOURS	[illegible]

*OPTIONAL

LUBRICATION CHART

TRACTOR, WHEEL TYPE

INTERVAL HOURS	POINT	IDENTIFICATION	LUBRICANT
5	1	AIR CLEANER	E.O.
10	2	STEERING MECHANISM, LIFT MECHANISM	M.P.G.
50	3	CLUTCH THROW-OUT BEARING	M.P.G.
100	4	ENGINE OIL CHANGE	E.O.
250	5	STEERING GEAR HOUSING CHECK GENERATOR BEARINGS, DISTRIBUTOR	E.O.
500	6	REPACK FRONT WHEEL BEARINGS	M.P.G.
1000	7	TRANSMISSION OIL CHANGE TORQUE TUBE OIL CHANGE POWER STEERING RESERVOIR	M.P.L. E.O. SPEC. O

LUBRICANT ABBREVIATIONS

E.O. ENGINE OIL

M.P.G. MULTIPURPOSE-TYPE GREASE

M.P.L. MULTIPURPOSE-TYPE GEAR LUBRICANT

SPEC. O AUTOMATIC TRANSMISSION FLUID — TYPE A

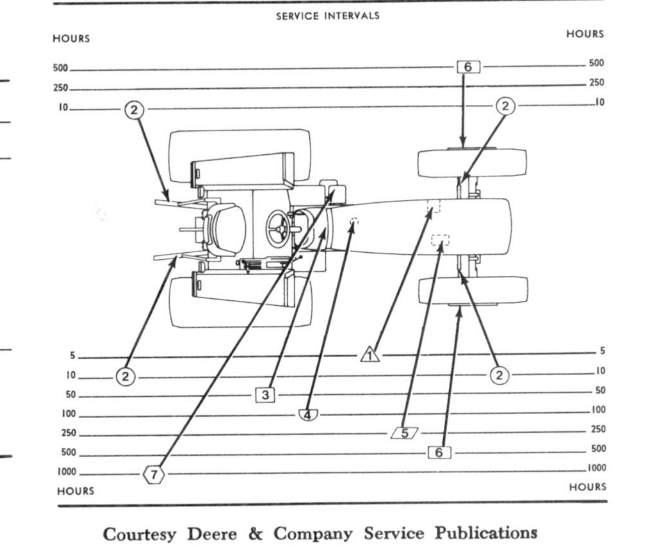

Courtesy Deere & Company Service Publications

Fig. 14-1—A lubrication chart showing the chassis lubrication points and the intervals between lubrication.

4. Lubricate the lower pedestal bearing at recommended intervals.
5. On wide front ends, lubricate tie rod ends, steering knuckles, axle pivots, and king-pins.

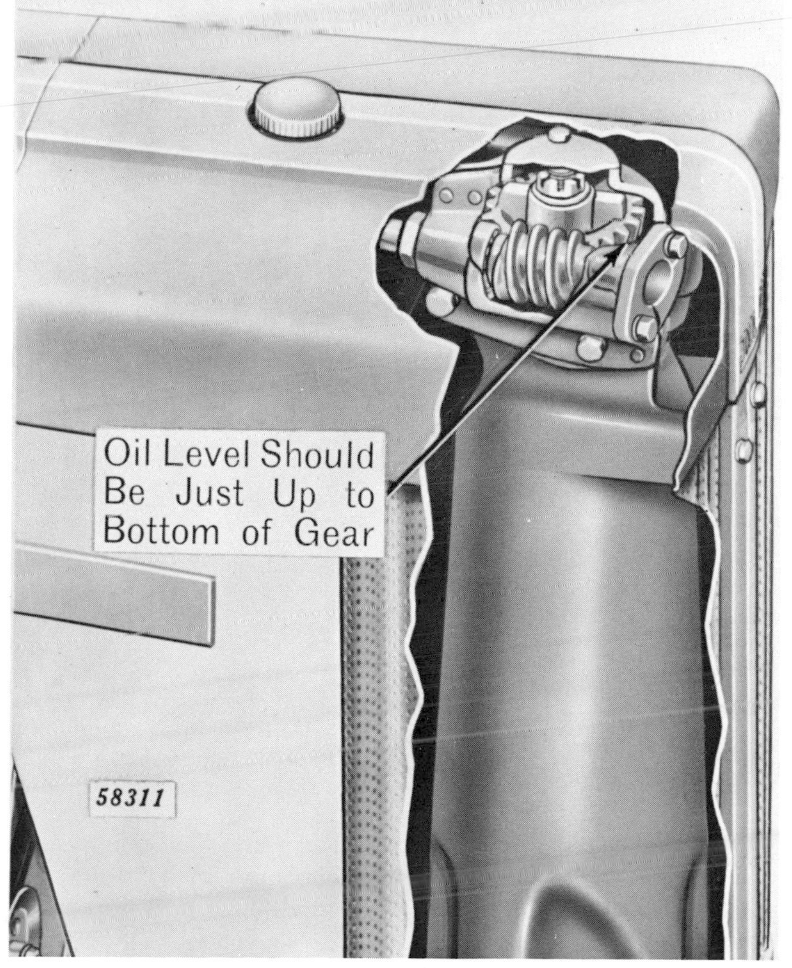

Courtesy John Deere, Moline, Ill.

Fig. 14-2—Steering gear oil level (manual steering).

Procedure—Power Steering

1. Drain and refill power steering reservoir at recommended intervals. (Consult the dealer for the correct fluid.)
2. Lubricate lower pedestal bearing.
3. On wide front ends, lubricate tie rod ends, steering knuckles, axle pivots, and king-pins.

Front Wheels

The front wheel bearings should be cleaned and repacked twice a year.

Courtesy American Oil Co.

Fig. 14-3—Greasing front wheel bearings is a commonly neglected service. These bearings rusted out because they were not greased.

A pressure gun fitting on the hub cap does not indicate that the bearings can be lubricated with a pressure gun. The fitting is placed there so that gun grease can be used if the tractor has been run through water or deep mud. Grease the wheels every 10 hours until they can be removed, cleaned and repacked with wheel bearing grease.

Adjust and Repack Front Wheels

Procedure

1. Jack up front of tractor and block it up.
2. Remove hub cap.
3. Remove cotter pin, lock nut, washer, bearing cone and bearing.
4. Remove the wheel.

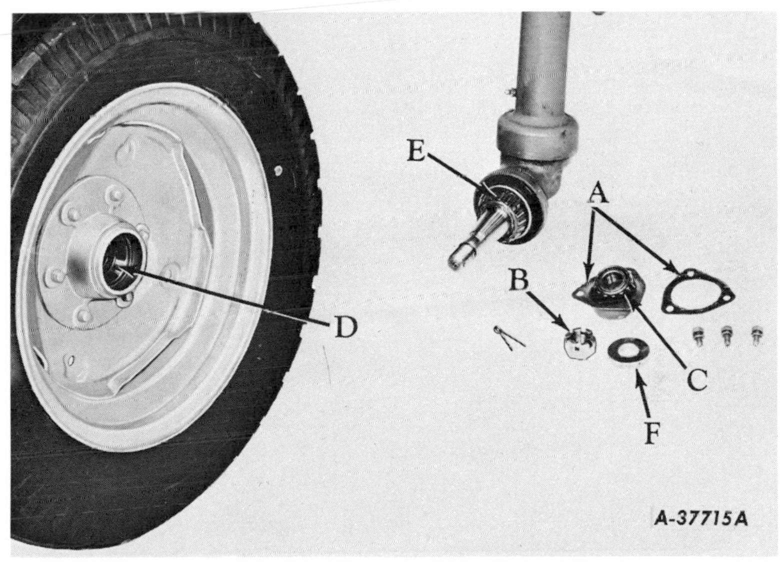

Courtesy International Harvester Co.

Fig. 14-4—Wheel removed for cleaning and greasing.

5. Remove inner bearing, dust seal and retainer.
   a. If the retainer is seated tightly, it may be necessary to drive out the inner cup in order to remove the seal retainer and bearing. Do this by inserting a long punch from the hub cap end of the hub. There are two notches on opposite sides of the hub that will permit the punch to just rest on the edge of the inner cup. Drive the cup out by pounding first on one side and then the other so the cup does not become wedged in the hub. Be careful to keep the punch from striking the bearing shell.

6. Wash bearings and hub in a safe solvent. Shake the bearings dry or use compressed air, but do not allow the bearings to spin, as this will damage them.
7. Inspect the bearings and cup. If either is worn, replace *both* the bearing and the cup.

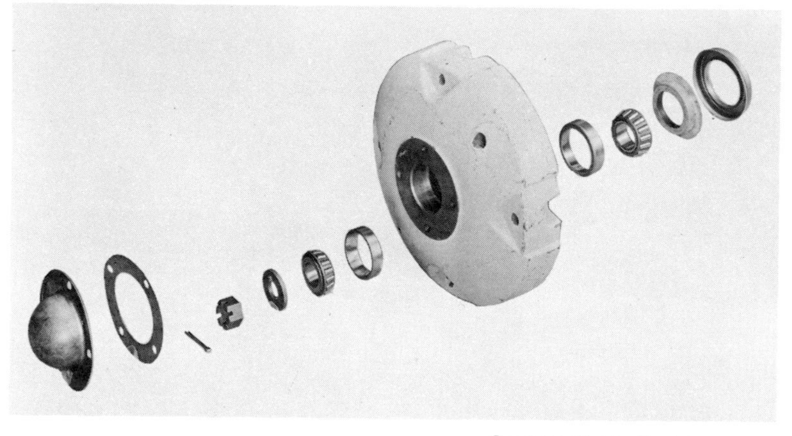

Courtesy Massey-Ferguson

Fig. 14-5—Disassembly of a front wheel.

8. Pack the bearings.
   a. Use wheel bearing grease. Some operators find an all-purpose grease satisfactory.
   b. Place grease in the palm of the hand and work the grease into the bearing until all spaces between the rollers are filled.
   c. Wrap the bearing in clean paper until ready to install. This will protect it from dust and dirt.
9. Examine the grease seals and grease retainer. Replace them if worn.
10. Replace inner cup by driving it into the hub with a small punch and hammer. Be sure the thick portion of the cup is toward the inside of the hub. Do not scratch the bearing surface with the punch.

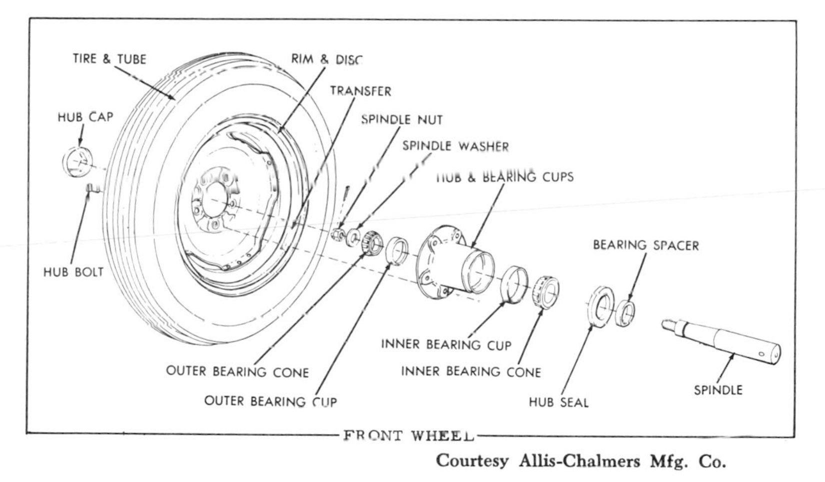

Courtesy Allis-Chalmers Mfg. Co.

Fig. 14-6–Parts of front wheel and hub.

Note–Do not fill the hub or hub cap with grease. The grease packed in the bearing will give sufficient lubrication until the bearing is repacked.

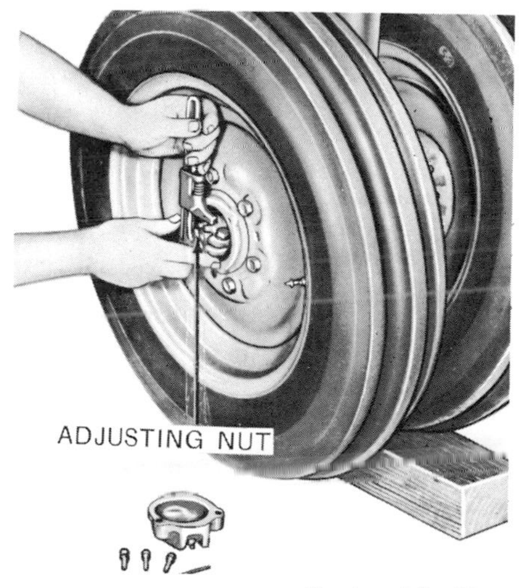

Courtesy John Deere, Moline, Ill.

Fig. 14-7–Adjusting front wheel bearing.

11. Replace bearings, seal retainer and seals.
12. Replace the wheel.
13. Adjust the wheel bearings.
    a. Draw the adjusting nut up tight, then back it off one full castellation, or notch, plus any additional amount necessary to insert the cotter pin.

Note—When a front mounted loader is used, the bearings may need to be adjusted tighter than this. Consult your dealer for the correct adjustment.

Rear Wheel Bearings

Rear wheel bearings are often lubricated by the lubricant in the final drive or differential case and require no further lubrication.

Some bearings are lubricated periodically by removing a small pipe plug and inserting a pressure gun fitting and pumping in a prescribed number of strokes of pressure gun grease. Follow the directions in the Operator's Manual for servicing this type of rear wheel bearing.

Tires

Correct inflation is the most important factor in reducing tire wear and damage.

Courtesy John Deere, Moline, Ill.

Fig. 14-8—Careless driving shortens tire life.

Underinflation permits the tire to flex too much, causing breaking of the sidewalls and uneven wear of tread.

Overinflation reduces traction, increases slippage, causes uneven tread wear and makes the tire susceptible to easy bruising.

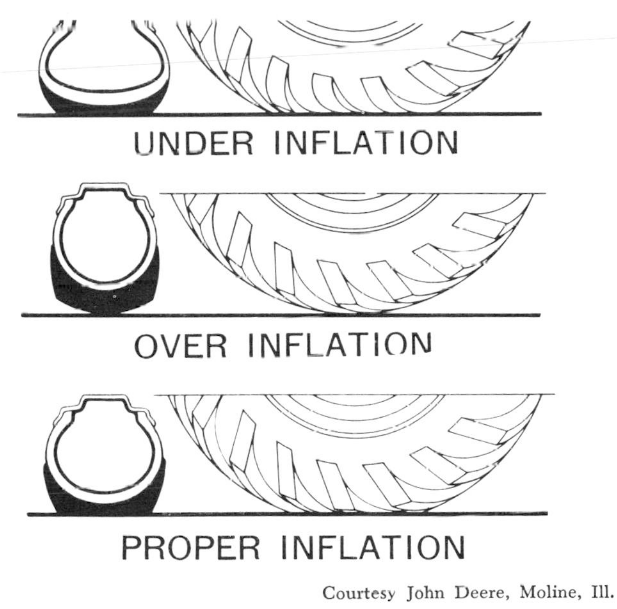

Courtesy John Deere, Moline, Ill.

Fig. 14-9—Proper tire inflation is very important.

Inspect the tires occasionally, keep them inflated and check for cuts and bruises. Have the tire repaired when damage is found.

Four ply front wheel tires require 28 pounds pressure. Six ply front wheel tires require 36 pounds pressure. Rear tires require from 12 to 16 pounds depending on the weight being carried. When plowing, the furrow wheel pressure should be increased about 4 pounds to compensate for the extra weight caused by the tractor being tilted toward the furrow.

The tires may be filled about three-fourths full of water to increase weight when more traction is needed. A calcium chloride and water solution should be used in the winter. Dealers are

Courtesy International Harvester Co.

Fig. 14-10—Mechanical disc-type brake.

equipped to mix and add the solution to tires. A special valve is needed to permit the air to escape from the tire while the solution is being added. A special tire gauge is needed to test air pressure in fluid filled tires.

Cast iron wheel weights may be bolted to the wheel for increased weight instead of using fluid in the tires, or both weights and fluid may be used.

Brakes

The brakes on a tractor are sometimes called turning-brakes because of their use in assisting to make sharp turns. The maintenance necessary is adjustment and an occasional replacement of the lining.

There are several types of brakes in use, including external band, internal expanding and disc. The adjustment is different on each of these types and the Operator's Manual should be checked for the correct adjustment procedure.

The brake linings will usually give several years of service unless used excessively and incorrectly adjusted.

Courtesy John Deere, Moline, Ill.

Fig. 14-11—Adjusting an internal expanding shoe type brake.

Courtesy Massey-Ferguson

Fig. 14-12—Adjusting double internal expanding self-energizing two shoe type brake.

WARNING—The brakes must be kept equalized by adjusting both pedals to the same position so that when locked together, both brakes will brake the same amount. If they are not equalized and are locked together, an attempt to make a sudden stop will throw the tractor sideways and cause it to overturn. This is a common cause of many fatal accidents.

The Frame

The various sections of the tractor are fastened together, usually, with hex head cap screws or heavy bolts. These screws or bolts must be kept tight to prevent loss of lubricant, misalignment of strategic parts and costly damage.

Go over these screws as the tractor is being serviced and *keep them tight.*

Courtesy International Harvester Co.

Fig. 14-13—Always latch the brake pedals together when driving on the highway or when driving in high gear. *Be sure* brakes are properly adjusted.

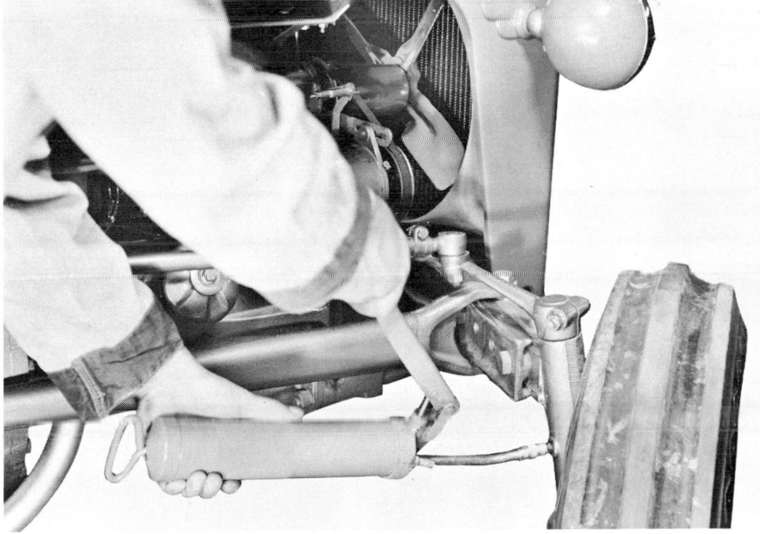

Courtesy Massey-Ferguson

Fig. 14-14—Lubricating the chassis with a grease gun.

Courtesy International Harvester Co.

Fig. 14-15—Don't oil or grease the tractor while the engine is running.

QUESTIONS

1. What component parts of a tractor make up the chassis?
2. What adjustments can be made on the steering mechanism?
3. How often should front wheel bearings be cleaned and repacked?
4. What lubricant should be used when packing front wheel bearings?
5. What adjustment is necessary on front wheel bearings?
6. Why is it necessary to keep the brakes equalized for safe operation of the tractor?
7. What maintenance is needed on the tractor frame?

Part III

OPERATION, REPAIR AND STORAGE

CHAPTER 15

OPERATING THE TRACTOR

See that the radiator is full of clean soft water or antifreeze to protect it at the lowest expected temperature.

See that the crank case has sufficient clean high grade engine oil of the proper viscosity.

See that the fuel tank has sufficient correct fuel.

See that the transmission and differential have sufficient correct grade oil.

See that all bearings are properly lubricated.

See that all rubber tires are inflated to the proper pressure.

Do not clean tractor or parts with gasoline, especially indoors, because of the fire hazard. Use a heavy fuel, or a commercial cleaner.

Courtesy John Deere, Moline, Ill.

Fig. 15-1—Your tractor will respond to careful treatment.

Keep the radiator fins and outside of engine free from dirt, chaff, and dust.

Do not overload the tractor.

Courtesy John Deere, Moline, Ill.

Fig. 15-2—An overloaded tractor will have a short service life.

Overloading

Your tractor is designed and built to handle economically and efficiently all jobs within its range of power. The use of any tractor on loads beyond its power range results in undue strain on all parts, and will, if continued, result in unnecessary repair expense and impaired efficiency of operation.—Tractor Instruction Book—John Deere, Moline, Ill.

If the wheels are frozen down, start the tractor backwards to break it out. Back the tractor up steep inclines to prevent upsetting.

Courtesy International Harvester Co.

Fig. 15-3—Always drive the tractor at speeds slow enough to insure safety, especially over rough ground or near ditches.

Keep the speed of the tractor down to safe limits, especially on rough ground or on turns.

Courtesy John Deere, Moline, Ill.

Fig. 15-4—CAUTION: Fast driving is the cause of many accidents. Drive at a safe speed at all times.

Be sure both brakes take hold at the same time on straightaway operation, especially at the higher speeds.

In cold weather operations use a radiator curtain or shutter in addition to a thermostat.

Tighten all nuts and studs frequently, especially on wheel lugs, steering rings, and draw bar.

Make major repairs or adjustments only on the advice of an expert mechanic.

Keep the oil filter clean and operating at its greatest efficiency.

Clean out the fuel sediment bulb occasionally. Drain the carburetor bowl occasionally.

Keep the air-cleaner clean and functioning at its greatest efficiency.

Check for and stop air leaks between the air cleaner and the carburetor.

Keep a sharp lookout for fuel, oil, and water leaks.

Courtesy John Deere, Moline, Ill.

Fig. 15-5—CAUTION: Do not stand between the tractor and implement unless the shift lever is in "park" position to hold the tractor stationary.

Do not back the tractor into an implement while standing between the tractor and implement. Sit on the seat and handle the implement tongue with a hook.

Courtesy International Harvester Co.

Fig. 15-6—When hitching to an implement standing on sloping ground, be sure tractor brakes are set and locked.

When in doubt about a procedure or practice follow the manufacturer's instruction book.

Go over the tractor during slack time and make repairs and adjustments. This will save expensive time later.

Never put off making a needed repair or an adjustment until some more convenient time.

Keep the spark plugs cleaned and correctly adjusted. Keep dust and dirt wiped from the spark plug insulators.

Keep enough wheel weights on rubber tires to prevent excessive slippage.

Keep the magneto or distributor breaker points clean and properly spaced.

Do not run V belts too tight.

Keep valve tappets properly adjusted.

Always allow engine to warm up before putting it to heavy or fast work.

Be sure clutch does not slip.

When operating a rubber-tired tractor at belt work, be sure the frame of the tractor is grounded.

Do not engage power take-off or belt pulley on most tractors while the tractor is in motion.

Keep the crankcase breather cap cleaned and oiled.

Do not continue to operate an engine that knocks continually. Check on the cause and remedy it.

Do not use cheap, low octane fuel in a high compression engine.

Always engage the clutch slowly enough to insure a smooth start.

Fill the fuel tank in the evening after a day's use, rather than in the morning.

Remove fuel from above the bottom of a storage tank rather than from the bottom.

Courtesy International Harvester Co.

Fig. 15-7—Always engage the clutch gently, especially when going up a hill or pulling out of a ditch.

Courtesy International Harvester Co.

Fig. 15-8—Only one person, the operator, should be permitted to ride on the tractor when it is in operation.

Courtesy John Deere, Moline, Ill.

Fig. 15-9—When more than one person attempts to ride on a tractor, someone is likely to get hurt.

Never run engine with choke out.

Do not pull heavy loads from any other point than the draw bar.

Do not fill tank with gasoline if there is a lantern or open flame near.

Be sure the funnel or hose nozzle is in contact with the tank at all times while filling with gasoline.

Have engine stopped while filling the tank.

Do not ride, nor allow anyone else to ride, on the tractor except on the seat.

Do not pour cold water into the radiator of an overheated engine.

Courtesy International Harvester Co.

Fig. 15-10—If the motor overheats, allow the engine to cool off before removing the cap. When removing the cap, be extremely careful to avoid being scalded by steam.

Do not try to repair, adjust or clean out a tractor or implement that is in motion.

Dirt is the number one enemy of your tractor, keep it out.

The operator has more to do with long life and satisfactory service of a tractor than any other one factor. Be a good operator.

A few minutes of maintenance a day will keep an expensive mechanic away.

Courtesy National Safety Council

Fig. 15-11—It is better to avoid an accident than to explain it.

WORLDWIDE SYMBOLS FOR OPERATOR CONTROLS

Symbols instead of words; that's what John Deere is using to promote worldwide identification of operator controls. Once standardized, they give a quick, positive message anywhere in the world — without translation. Study the symbols below and learn to recognize them at a glance.

Courtesy John Deere, Moline, Ill.

Fig. 15-12—Worldwide symbols for operator controls.

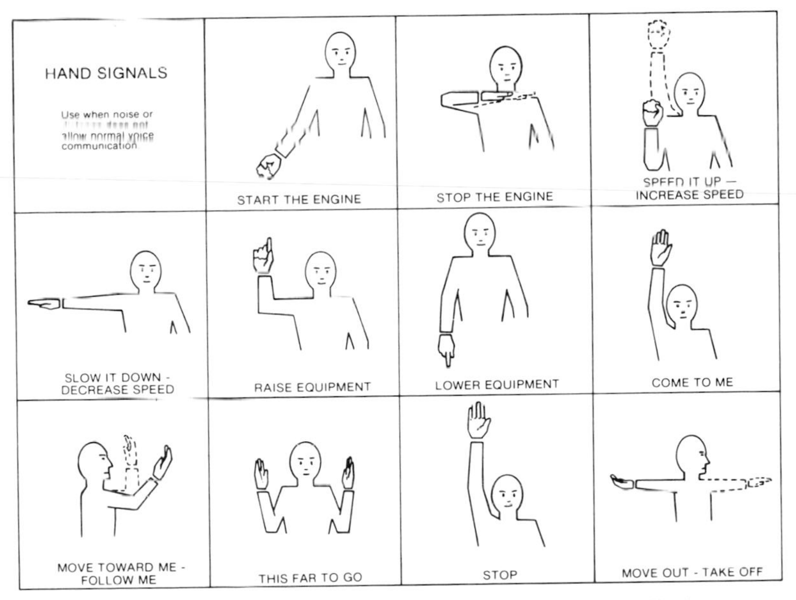

Courtesy Deere & Company Service Publications

Fig. 15-13—Hand signals.

If you are not an expert mechanic do not try to substitute for one.

The manufacturer has done his best; the rest is up to the operator. Be a good one.

Don't take chances. Be careful—hospitals and graves are full of careless people.

CHAPTER 16

OPERATING THE TRACTOR IN COLD WEATHER

1. Use winter-grade lubricants.
2. Use lighter-weight crankcase oil.
3. Use a lightweight oil in air cleaner oil cup and in fuel injection pumps on diesel engines. Use the same grade as that used in the crankcase. Special diesel engine oil should not be used in air cleaners.
4. Use a winter grade transmission oil.
5. Fill fuel tank at end of day's run to prevent moisture collecting in the tank.
6. Momentarily loosen the oil drain plug in the bottom of oil pan to allow possible water accumulation to drain off; tighten plug after water has drained off and when the oil, which will float on top of the water, first appears or starts to drain.
7. Keep the engine warm by using a radiator cover or by installing a shutter.
8. Keep the battery well charged. A badly discharged battery will freeze more quickly than one that is well charged.
9. Drain the radiator and engine after each day's run if an anti-freeze solution is not used.
10. If an anti-freeze solution is used in the cooling system, check frequently and replenish when necessary.

CHAPTER 17

OPERATING THE TRACTOR SAFELY

(Prepared by the Farm Safety Committee of the Farm Equipment Institute and approved by the National Safety Council, Inc.)

1. Be sure the gear shift lever is in neutral before cranking the engine.
2. Always engage the clutch gently, especially when going up a hill or pulling out of a ditch.

Courtesy International Harvester Co.

Fig. 17-1—Be sure gearshift lever is in neutral before starting the engine.

3. When driving on highways, or to and from fields, be sure that both wheels are braked simultaneously when making an emergency stop.
4. Always ride on seat or stand on platform of tractor. Never ride on drawbar of tractor or drawn implement.

Courtesy John Deere, Moline, Ill.

Fig. 17-2—CAUTION: Use warning lamps when driving at night.

Courtesy International Harvester Co.

Fig. 17-3—Always ride on the tractor seat.

5. When tractor is hitched to a stump or heavy load, always hitch to drawbar and never take up the slack of chain with a jerk.

Courtesy International Harvester Co.

Fig. 17-4—Always hitch to the drawbar and never take up the slack with a jerk.

Courtesy John Deere, Moline, Ill.

Fig. 17-5—Never drive too close to ditches.

6. Be extra careful when working on hillsides. Watch out for holes or ditches into which a wheel may drop and cause tractor to overturn.

Courtesy International Harvester Co.

Fig. 17-6—Always keep tractor in gear when going down steep grades.

Courtesy John Deere, Moline, Ill.

Fig. 17-7—Do not race along highways, observe all traffic rules.

7. Always keep tractor in gear when going down steep hills or grades.

Courtesy International Harvester Co.

Fig. 17-8–Reduce speed before making a turn.

8. Always drive tractor at speeds slow enough to insure safety, especially over rough ground or near ditches.
9. Reduce speed before making a turn or applying brakes. The hazard of overturning the tractor increases four times when speed is doubled.

Courtesy International Harvester Co.

Fig. 17-9–Always stop power take-off before dismounting from the tractor.

10. Always stop power take-off before dismounting from tractor.
11. Never dismount from tractor when it is motion. Wait until it stops.

Courtesy International Harvester Co.

Fig. 17-10—Never dismount from the tractor while it is in motion. Wait until it stops.

Courtesy John Deere, Moline, Ill.

Fig. 17-11—Never install or remove a belt while pulley is in motion.

12. Never permit persons other than the driver to ride on tractor when it is in operation.

Courtesy John Deere, Moline, Ill.

Fig. 17-12–CAUTION: Make sure the tractor engine is stopped and the shift lever in the "park" position. The PTO shaft should never be turned by hand with the engine running.

Courtesy John Deere, Moline, Ill.

Fig. 17-13–Never wear loose clothing around power shaft.

Courtesy John Deere, Moline, Ill.

Fig. 17-14–CAUTION: Before starting the tractor engine, be sure there is plenty of ventilation. Never operate the tractor in a shed or garage.

Courtesy John Deere, Moline, Ill.

Fig. 17-15–Use extreme care when transporting heavy rear-mounted implements.

Courtesy National Safety Council

Fig. 17-16—Accidents don't have to happen!

13. Never stand between tractor and drawn implement when hitching. Use an iron hook to handle drawbar.
14. Do not put on or remove belt from belt pulley while the pulley is in motion.
15. Should motor overheat be careful when refilling radiator.
16. Never refuel tractor while motor is running or extremely hot.
17. When tractor is attached to a power implement be sure that all power line shielding is in place.

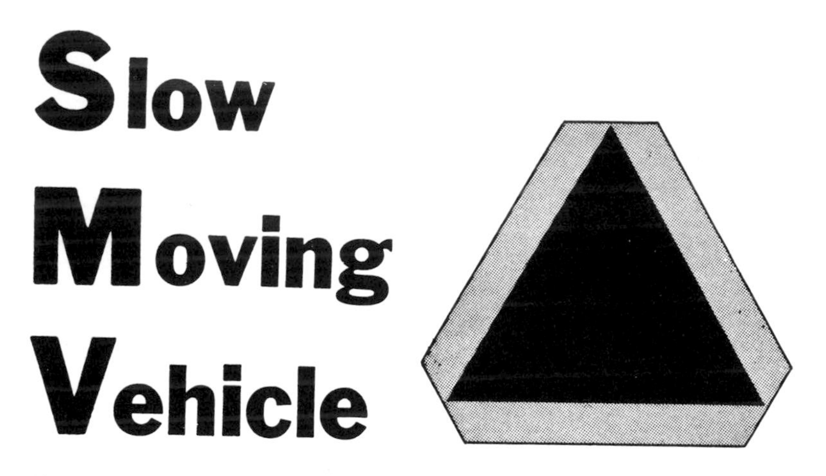

Fig. 17-17—For your protection and safety, display the Slow Moving Vehicle emblem on the back of all tractors and implements. The SMV emblem is required in many states.

Courtesy International Harvester Co.

Fig. 17-18–A general purpose tractor with a roll over protective system.

Remember . . . a CAREFUL OPERATOR always is the BEST INSURANCE against an accident.

Fig. 17-19.

CHAPTER 18

REPAIRING THE ENGINE

Preventive maintenance will increase the life of all engine parts and reduce wear to a minimum; however, normal wear will take place and eventually minor repairs will be needed, and, with continued use, major repairs will become necessary.

Minor repairs include such jobs as grinding or replacing valves, installing new piston rings, installing connecting rod bearings, installing main bearings and replacing ignition points. Even the minor repair jobs should be done by a competent mechanic with adequate special equipment. The dealer can usually supply such service.

Major repairs include such jobs as replacing sleeves or reboring cylinders, replacing timing gears, installing new pistons, replacing the crankshaft and main bearings, replacing valve guides and inserts, and any major work on gears or final drive. This work should always be done by a good mechanic in a well equipped repair shop.

The advice of a good mechanic should be sought when deciding when minor or major repairs are needed. It is costly to neglect needed repairs, because worn parts fail completely causing unnecessary breakage and damage to other parts of the engine. Waiting until a repair job *must* be done, to keep the engine running, will usually double or triple the cost of the repair.

Compression Testing

A test of the compression in each cylinder will give some indication of the condition of the valves and piston rings. A compression gauge is inserted into each cylinder in turn, with all spark plugs removed. As the engine is cranked, the gauge shows

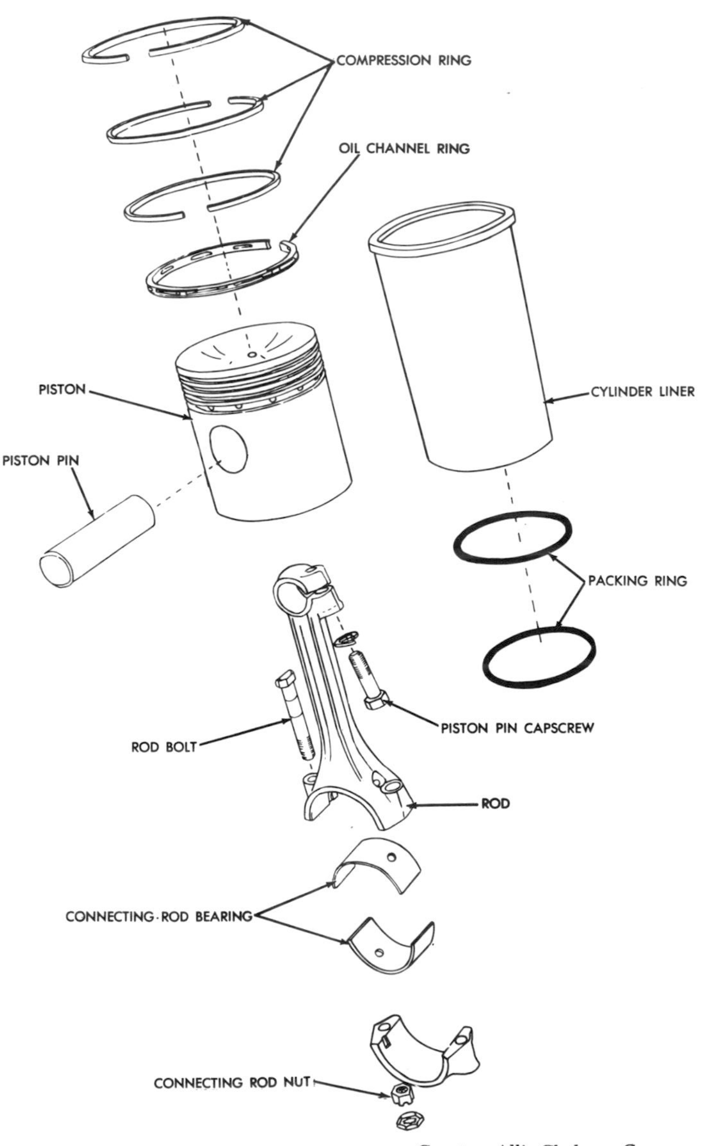

Courtesy Allis-Chalmers Corp.

Fig. 18-1—Piston and connecting rod work on these parts of the engine should be done by a well-trained mechanic.

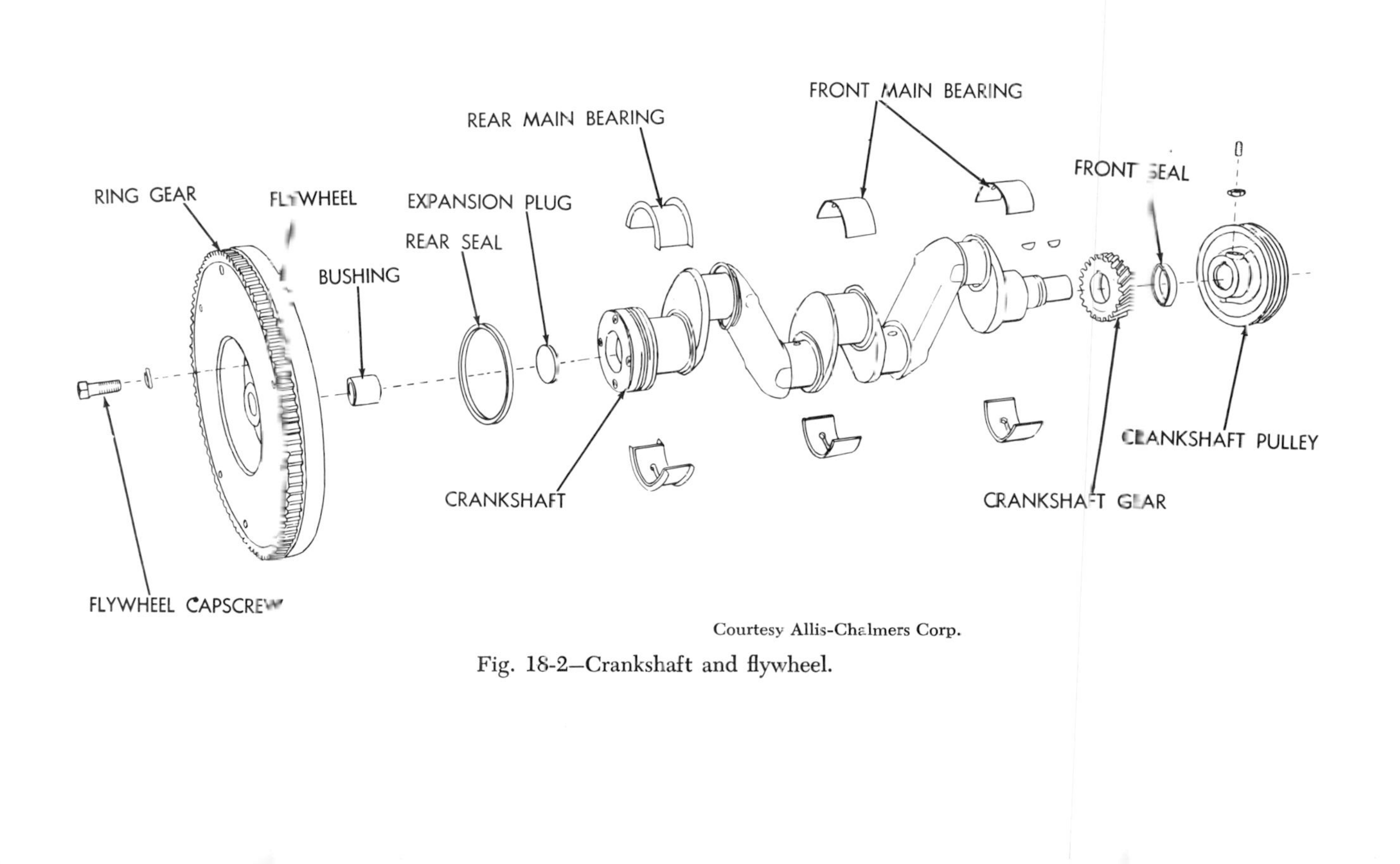

Courtesy Allis-Chalmers Corp.

Fig. 18-2—Crankshaft and flywheel.

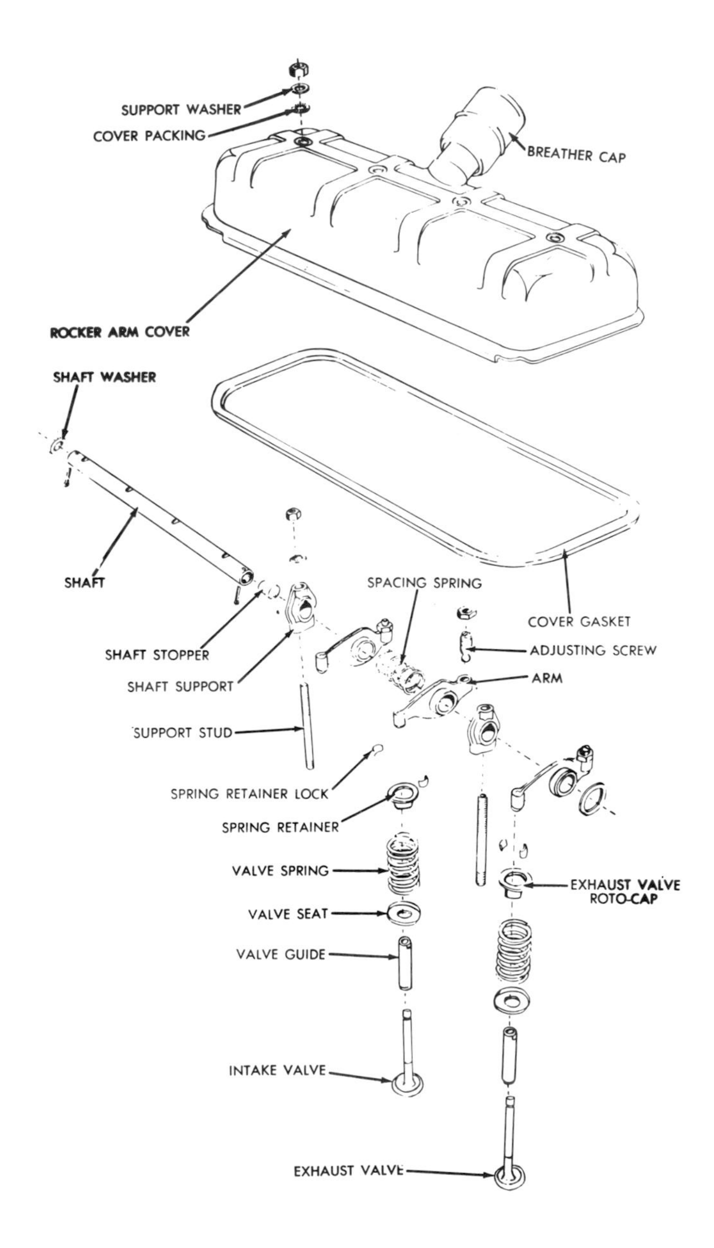

Courtesy Allis-Chalmers Corp.

Fig. 18-3—Overhead valve and rocker arm assembly.

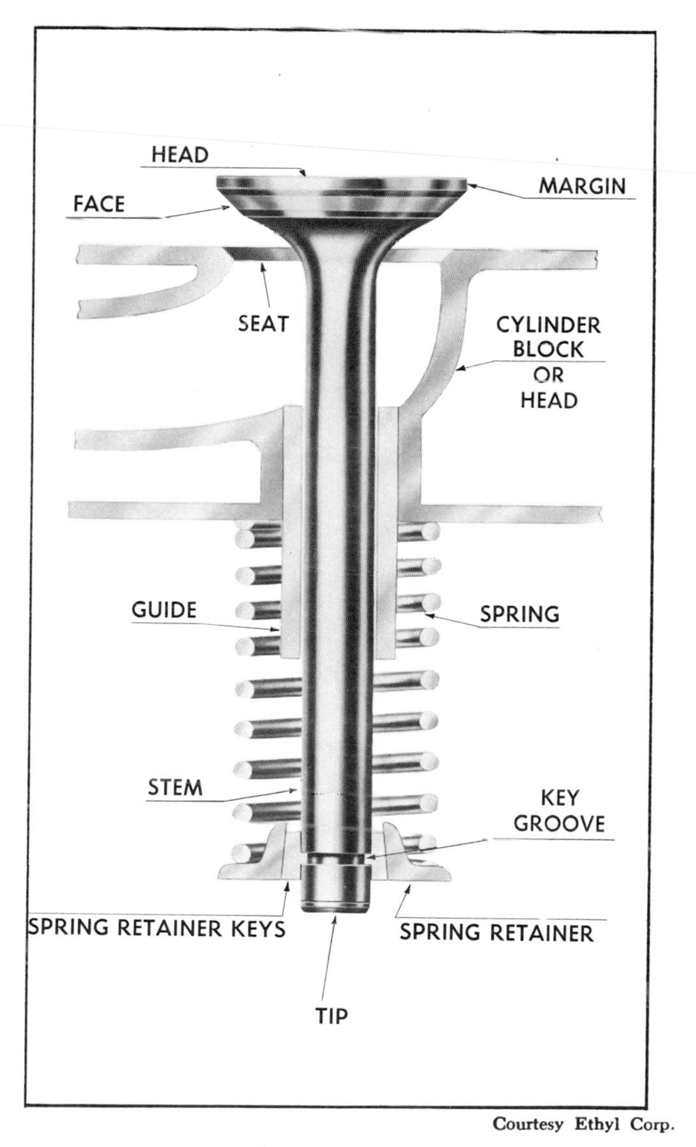

Courtesy Ethyl Corp.

Fig. 18-4—Valve assembly nomenclature.

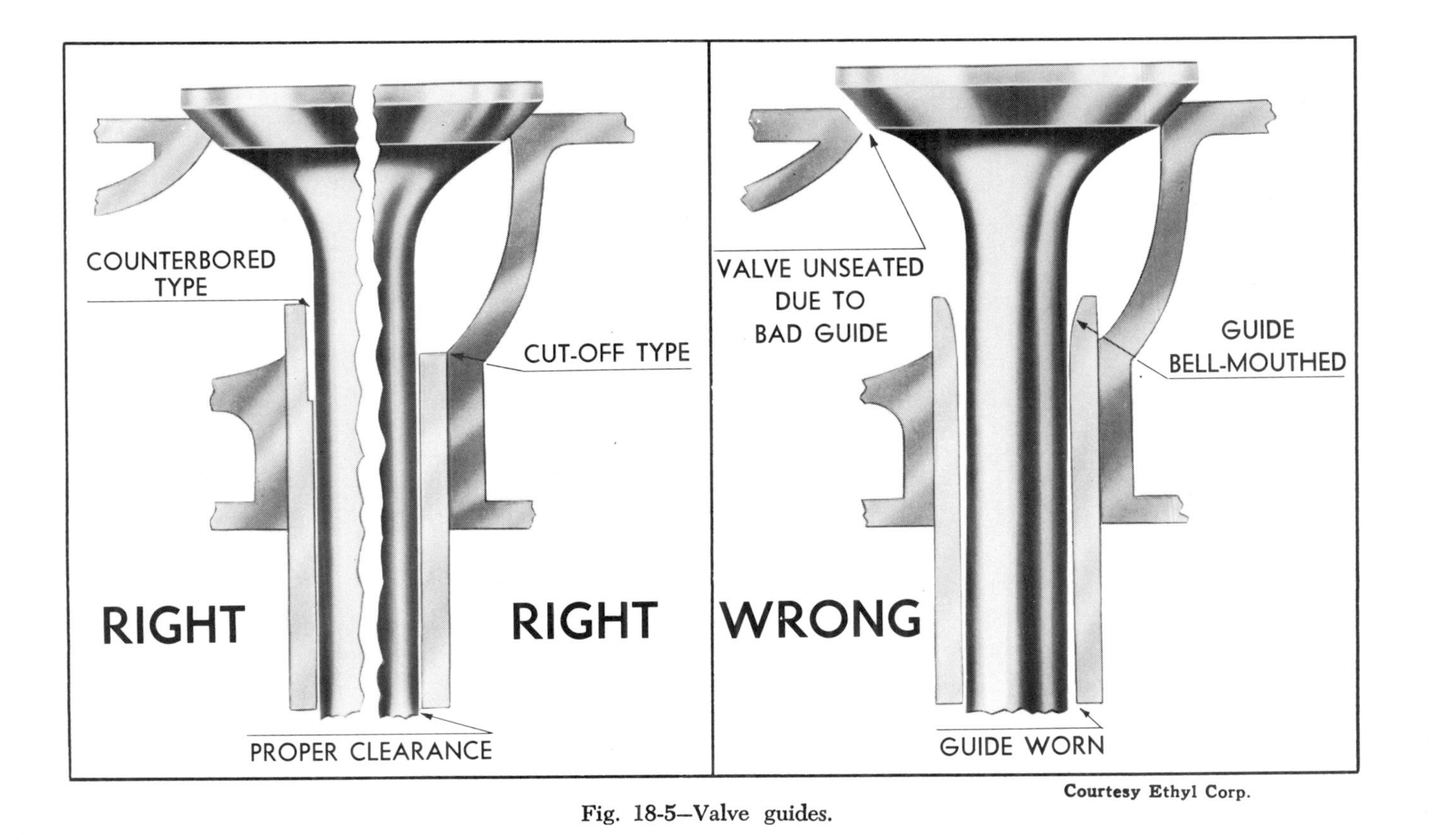

Courtesy Ethyl Corp.

Fig. 18-5—Valve guides.

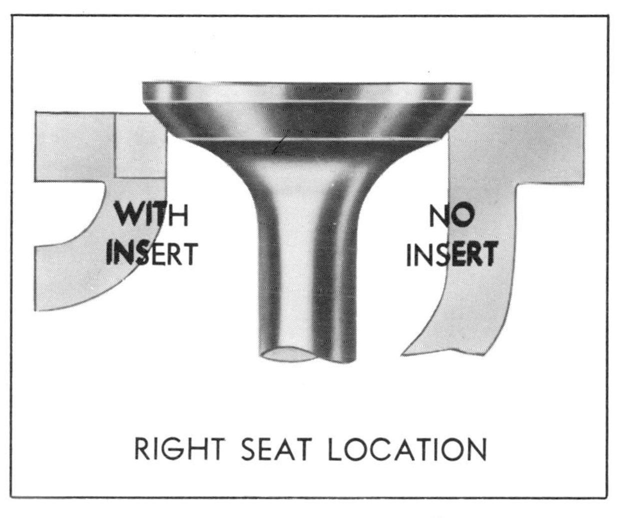

Courtesy Ethyl Corp.

Fig. 18-6—Correct seat location.

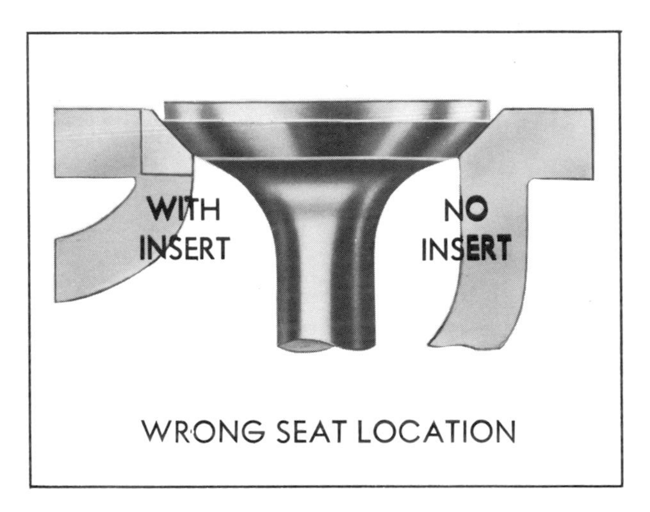

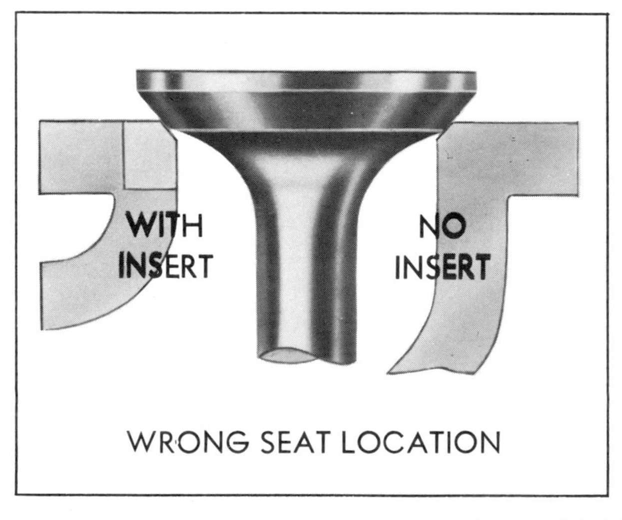

Courtesy Ethyl Corp.

Fig. 18-7—Incorrect seat locations.

Courtesy Ethyl Corp.

Fig. 18-8—Valve refacing.

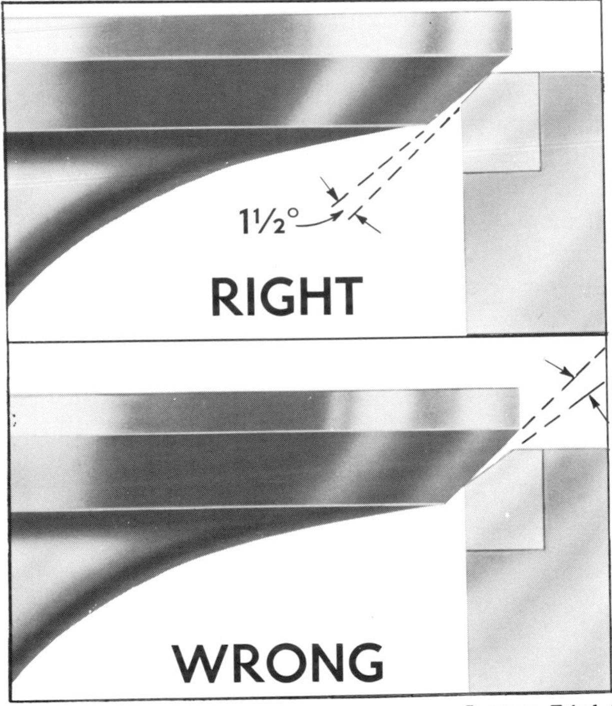

Courtesy Ethyl Corp.

Fig. 18-9—Interference angle.

Courtesy Sun Electric Corp.

Fig. 18-10—Compression pressure gauge.

the pressure that builds up in each cylinder. The pressure should be about the same in each cylinder. If the reading is low in a cylinder, it indicates a leak around a valve or past the rings. In order to determine whether the valves or rings are faulty, some motor oil should be placed in the cylinder and another test made. If the rings are bad, the oil will temporarily seal them and a higher pressure reading will be obtained. If the reading remains the same, a leaky valve is indicated.

Valve Rotators

A mechanism to rotate or permit the exhaust valves to rotate is being installed in many of the new tractor engines for the

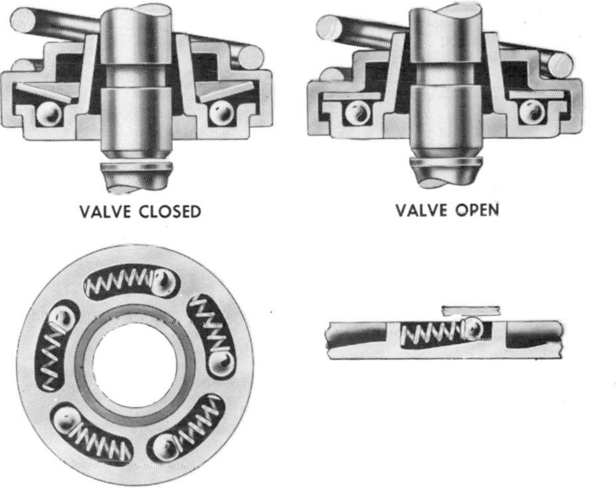

Courtesy Ethyl Corp.

Fig. 18-11—Positive type valve rotator.

purpose of increasing exhaust valve life. The valve rotates gradually which tends to wipe any carbon deposit off the valve seat. The rotating mechanism should be checked carefully when the valves are ground to make sure it is functioning properly.

Valve Adjustment

Valve life depends on the valve being able to close completely against the seat to seal off the hot exhaust gases. When the valve

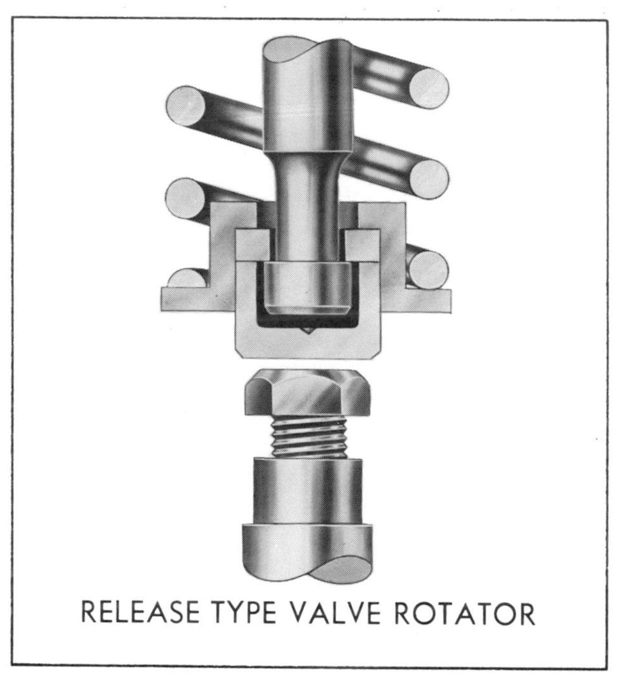

Courtesy Ethyl Corp.

Fig. 18-12—Release type valve rotator.

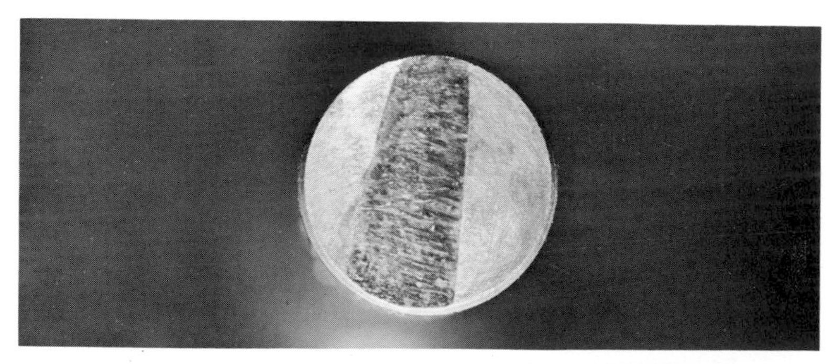

Courtesy American Oil Co.

Fig. 18-13—This valve failed to rotate as indicated by the tip.

Courtesy American Oil Co.

Fig. 18-14—Sludged pistons due to a leaky cylinder head gasket. The use of a torque wrench in tightening head bolts helps to prevent this.

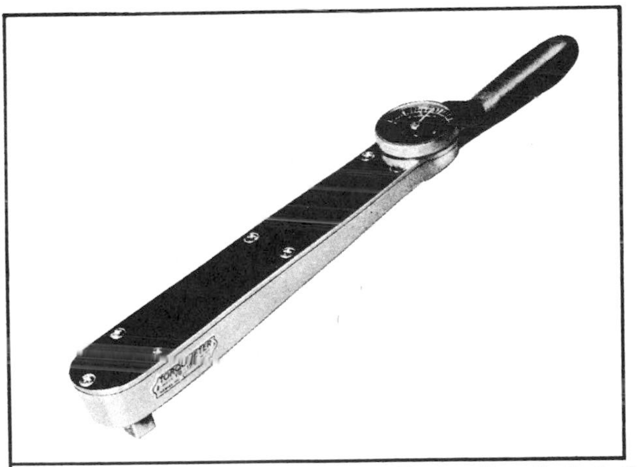

Courtesy Snap-On Tools Corp.

Fig. 18-15—A torque wrench should always be used when installing a head on an engine. Failure to tighten head bolts to the specified torque may result in head gasket failure and valve seat and cylinder bore distortion leading to poor valve and ring life.

Courtesy American Oil Co.

Fig. 18-16—The face of this valve shows evidence of burning. Insufficient valve tappet clearance could be the cause.

holds open because of insufficient valve tappet clearance, rapid burning of the valve will take place.

The intervals between valve clearance checks will vary with makes of tractors and with the age of the engine. On a new or overhauled engine, the clearance should be checked after about 50 hours and then every 150 hours until the clearance remains the same between two checks. Periodic checks of the valve clearance should be made every 400 to 500 hours following the initial run-in period.

The specific directions in the Operator's Manual should be followed in making valve tappet adjustment. The Manual will give the clearance necessary and will specify whether the adjustment is made with the engine hot or cold.

The valve clearance will change when the cylinder head is tightened so the clearance should be checked at any time the head bolts are disturbed or tightened.

On most late model tractors the valves should not be checked or adjusted with the engine running. The feeler gauge between the valve stem and rocker arm will cause the valve to extend into the combustion chamber farther than normal when the valve opens with the engine running and may cause the valve to strike the piston. This may bend or break the valve and damage the piston.

Most manufacturers now recommend adjusting the valves on late model six cylinder tractors at only two positions of the crankshaft—at top dead center (TDC) with No. 1 cylinder on the compression stroke and at TDC with No. 6 on the compression

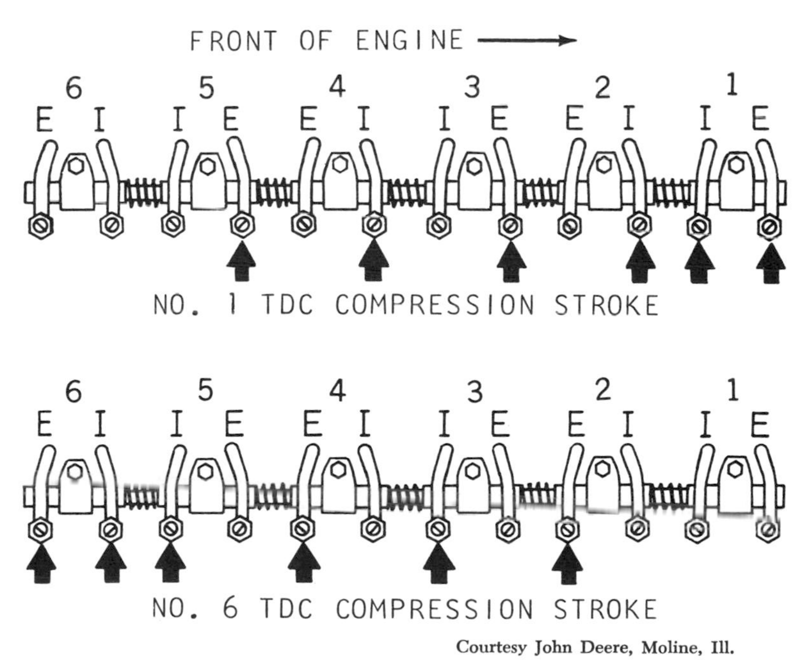

Courtesy John Deere, Moline, Ill.

Fig. 18-17—Valve adjusting sequence.

stroke. With No. 1 at TDC on the compression stroke, adjust the intake valves on No. 1, 2 and 4 cylinders and the exhaust valves No. 1, 3 and 5 cylinders. Turn the crankshaft one complete revolution, and with No. 6 cylinder at TDC on the compression stroke adjust the intake valves on No. 3, 5 and 6 cylinders and the exhaust valves on No. 2, 4 and 6 cylinders.

Another system of adjusting the valves in exactly the same way is to number the valves from the front of the engine and adjust valves numbered 1, 2, 3, 5, 7 and 9 with No. 1 cylinder at TDC on the compression stroke and adjust valves numbered 4, 6, 8, 10, 11 and 12 with No. 6 cylinder at TDC on the compression stroke.

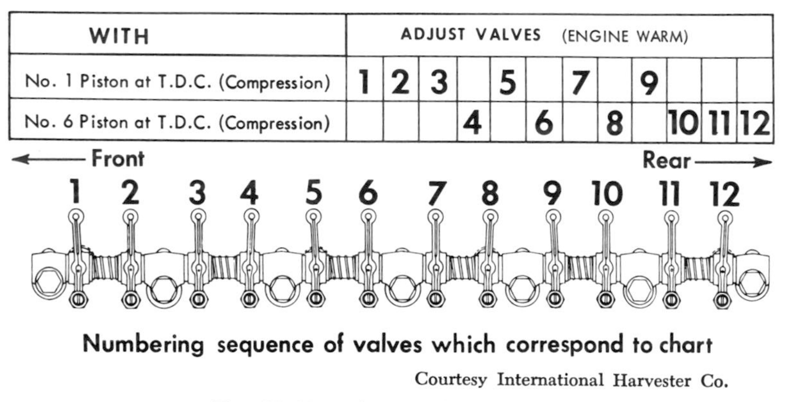

WITH	ADJUST VALVES (ENGINE WARM)											
No. 1 Piston at T.D.C. (Compression)	1	2	3		5		7		9			
No. 6 Piston at T.D.C. (Compression)				4		6		8		10	11	12

Courtesy International Harvester Co.

Fig. 18-18—Valve numbering sequence.

This method of adjusting valves is accurate, if done carefully, and the crankshaft has to be turned only one complete revolution.

The TDC mark on the flywheel or fan drive pulley will line up with the pointer or reference mark at each revolution of the crankshaft when No. 1 and No. 6 cylinders are at the TDC position in a six cylinder engine with a firing order of 1, 5, 3, 6, 2, 4. Either No. 1 or No. 6 cylinder is on the compression stroke and the valve adjustment may be started on the correct valves. To assist in determining which cylinder is on the compression stroke it is helpful to know that when No. 1 cylinder is at TDC on the compression stroke the exhaust valve on No. 2 cylinder will be partially open and the rocker arm cannot be moved by hand. When No. 6 cylinder is at TDC on the compression stroke the

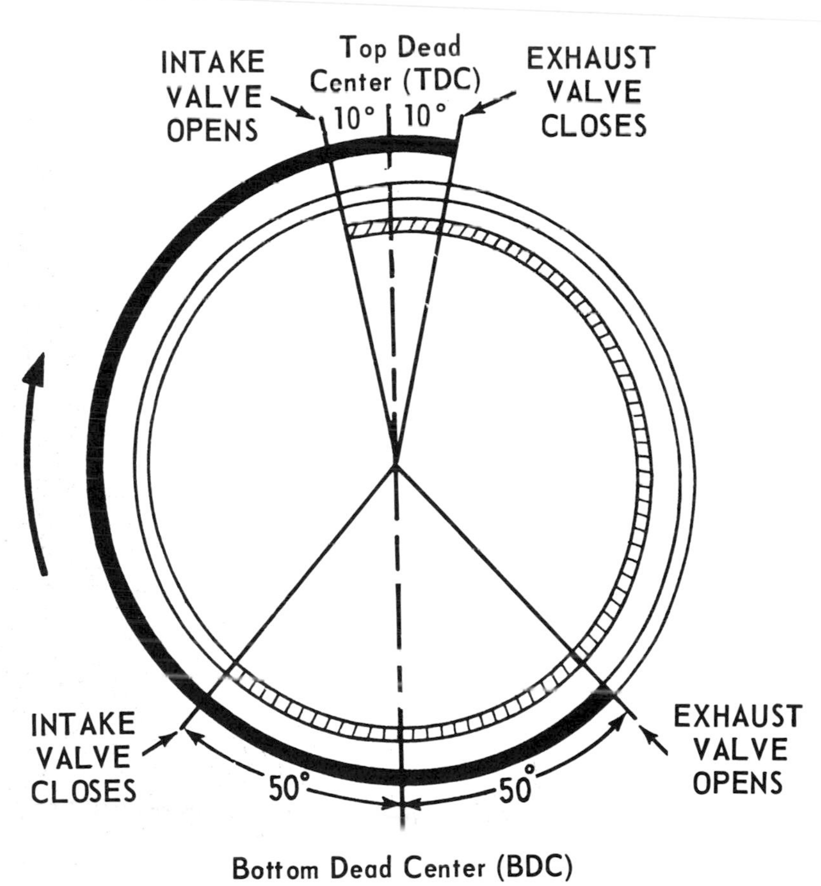

Courtesy **John Deere, Moline, Ill.**

Fig. 18-19—Typical valve timing diagram or spiral. Note the valve overlap at the end of the exhaust stroke when the intake valve has opened and the exhaust valve is still open. Both rocker arms are tight at this TDC position.

exhaust valve on No. 5 cylinder will be partially open and the rocker arm cannot be moved by hand. Both valves on any cylinder at TDC on the compression stroke will be closed, and the rocker arms can be moved slightly by hand if there is any valve clearance.

Adjusting valves at two crankshaft positions works equally well on a four or three cylinder engine but the instructions in the Operator's Manual must be followed exactly, because the valves to be adjusted at each crankshaft position will vary depending on the firing order. Some four cylinder engines have a firing order of 1, 2, 4, 3 and others have a firing order of 1, 3, 4, 2. Most three cylinder engines have a firing order of 1, 2, 3.

Another method of adjusting valves is to start with No. 1 cylinder at TDC on the compression stroke and adjust both

Courtesy John Deere, Moline, Ill.

Fig. 18-20—Turning the crankshaft to TDC with a large screwdriver.

valves on No. 1; then turn the crankshaft enough to bring the next cylinder in the firing order to TDC on the compression stroke and adjust both valves on that cylinder. Continue in this manner, following the firing order, until all valves on all cylinders have been adjusted. The crankshaft will have to be rotated two complete revolutions when using this method, and it is sometimes difficult to tell when each cylinder is at the TDC position, because the timing marks line up only when No. 1 is at TDC.

The complete reconditioning of an engine will include the pistons, rings and cylinders. The cylinders should be checked for taper and wear between the top and bottom in the ring travel area. Check to see if the cylinders are out-of-round. If the cylinder taper and out-of-roundness is greater than allowable, the cylinders will need to be rebored and honed or have new sleeves and pistons installed. Check the overhaul and repair manual for the recommended limit for maximum permissible cylinder wear.

Maximum cylinder wear normally occurs at the very top of top ring travel. For most accurate results, the cylinder should be measured at these points, both parallel and at right angles to the crankshaft, to determine out-of-roundness, maximum wear and cylinder taper. Use a dial gauge, inside micrometers or telescopic gauge and outside micrometers for cylinder measurement.

Procedure

1. Rotate crankshaft until piston is at bottom dead center.
2. Carefully measure the cylinder diameter immediately below the cylinder ridge.
3. Next, measure the cylinder diameter immediately above the piston head.
4. The difference between these two diameters is the approximate cylinder taper.
5. The difference between measurements made parallel and at right angles to the crankshaft is the approximate out-of-roundness.

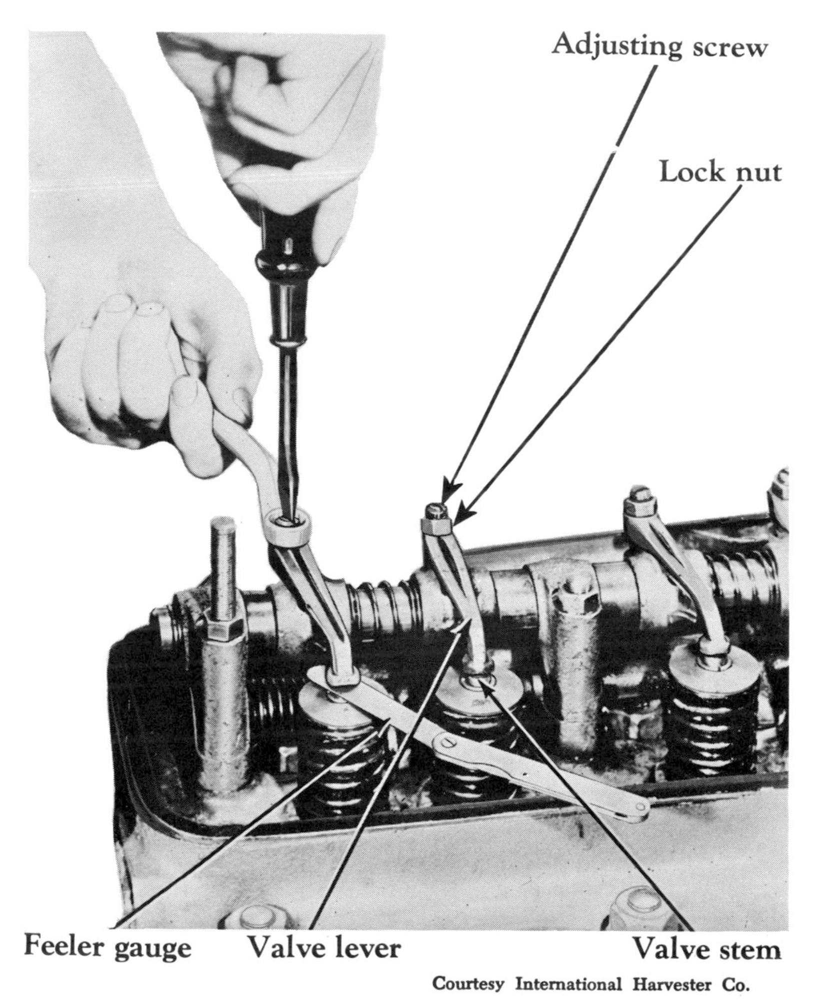

Courtesy International Harvester Co.

Fig. 18-21—Adjusting the valve tappet clearance.

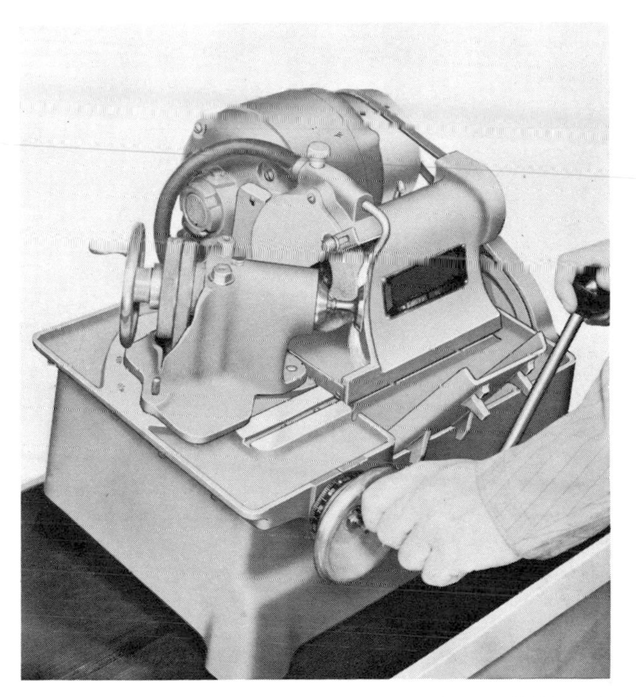

Courtesy Hall-Toledo, Inc.

Fig. 18-22—Valve refacing machine. One example of specialized equipment necessary to do a good valve job.

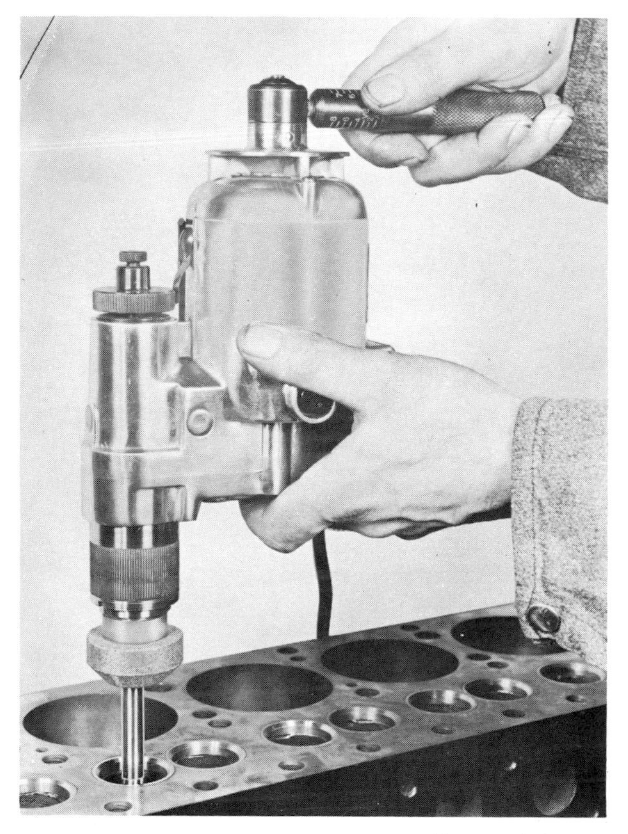

Courtesy Hall-Toledo, Inc.

Fig. 18-23—Eccentric type valve seat grinder. Another special piece of equipment found in a well equipped repair shop.

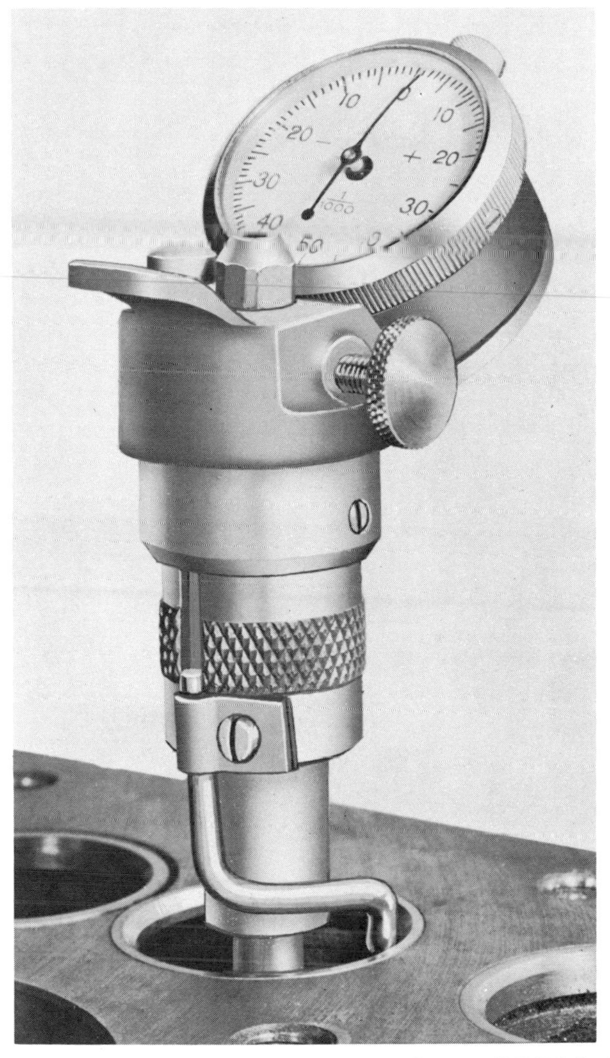

Courtesy Hall-Toledo, Inc.

Fig. 18-24—Valve seat dial gauge. A valve reconditioning tool of the expert mechanic to test trueness of the valve seat.

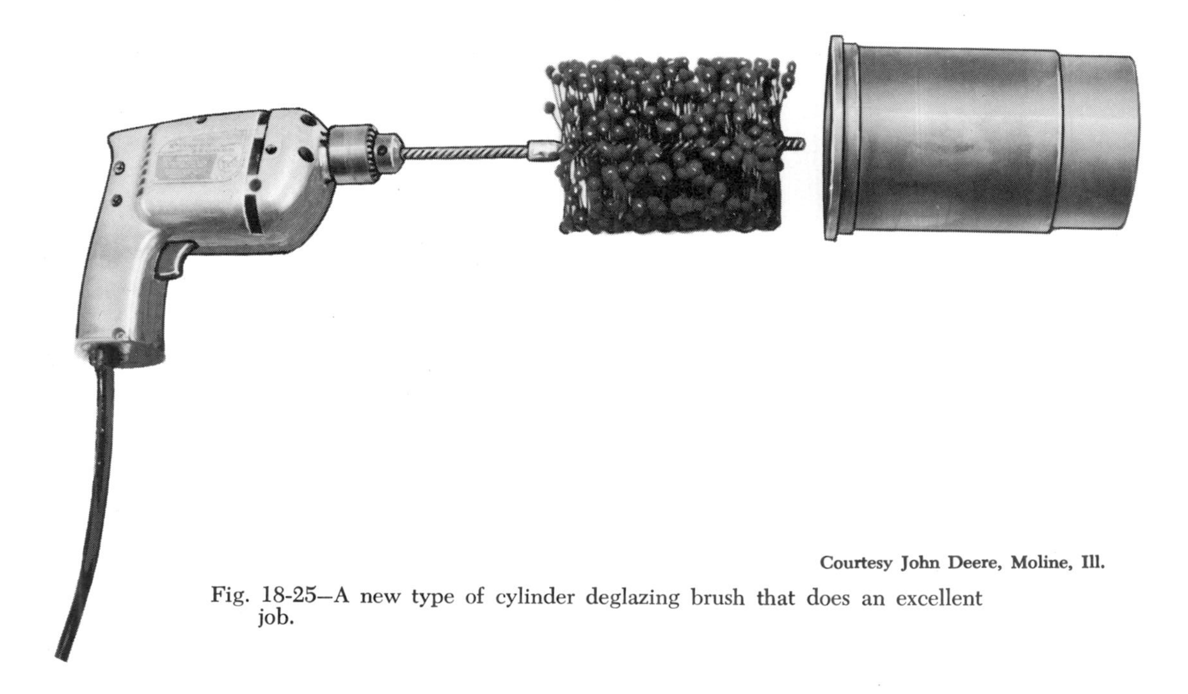

Courtesy John Deere, Moline, Ill.

Fig. 18-25—A new type of cylinder deglazing brush that does an excellent job.

When the decision is made to rering the engine, the cylinder ridge must be removed before the pistons are removed if the ridge is excessive. This eliminates the possibility of damaging piston lands during piston removal and prevents chips and carbon deposits from dropping on the crankshaft. A measurement of cylinder diameter above and immediately below the ridge will determine whether cylinder ridge is excessive. If the difference between the two diameters measures less than .004", the ridge

Courtesy Dana Corp., manufacturer of Perfect Circle Piston Rings

Fig. 18 26 Properly honed cylinder surfaces will have a crosshatch pattern as shown here. This may be done with a cylinder hone or with a cylinder deglazing brush.

need not be removed. When the diameter difference is .004″ or more, clean deposits from the ridge area and the top of the block and remove ridges with a suitable ridge cutter or grinder. Do not cut down into the ring travel area when removing the cylinder ridge.

When reringing an engine, it is usually advisable to hone or deglaze the cylinder walls to help the new rings seat. The crosshatch pattern on the cylinder walls holds oil and lubricates the rings as they wear-in and seat to the cylinder wall.

Pistons with worn ring grooves will not be helped much by new rings. The engine will probably continue to use oil and the anticipated power will not be produced. Worn ring grooves can be repaired by remachining and installing a steel spacer above the top ring where wear usually is greatest.

Before installing new rings on a piston, push a compression ring from the set down to the lower unworn portion of each cylinder, making sure the ring is perpendicular to the vertical axis of the cylinder. Measure the end clearance (gap) of the ring and compare it with the clearance listed in the instruction sheet. Insufficient end clearance may cause scuffing, scoring, ring breakage or engine seizure when the ring expands as the engine warms up.

Oil from connecting rod bearings lubricates pistons and rings. During engine reconditioning, if only the connecting rod bearings are replaced, the lubrication system may become unbalanced. The corrected but *reduced* bearing clearance at the connecting rods, coupled with *increased* clearance at worn but uncorrected main and camshaft bearings, may reduce oil flow to the pistons and rings. The unbalanced system may flood camshaft and main bearing areas while starving pistons and rings.

The fastest and most accurate method for checking main and connecting rod bearing clearances is with a Perfect Circle Plastigage. This is a small round piece of plastic which is laid across the bearing. The bearing is then tightened to the recommended torque. When the bearing cap is removed, the Plastigage will be flattened somewhat and the width of the strip of plastic is com-

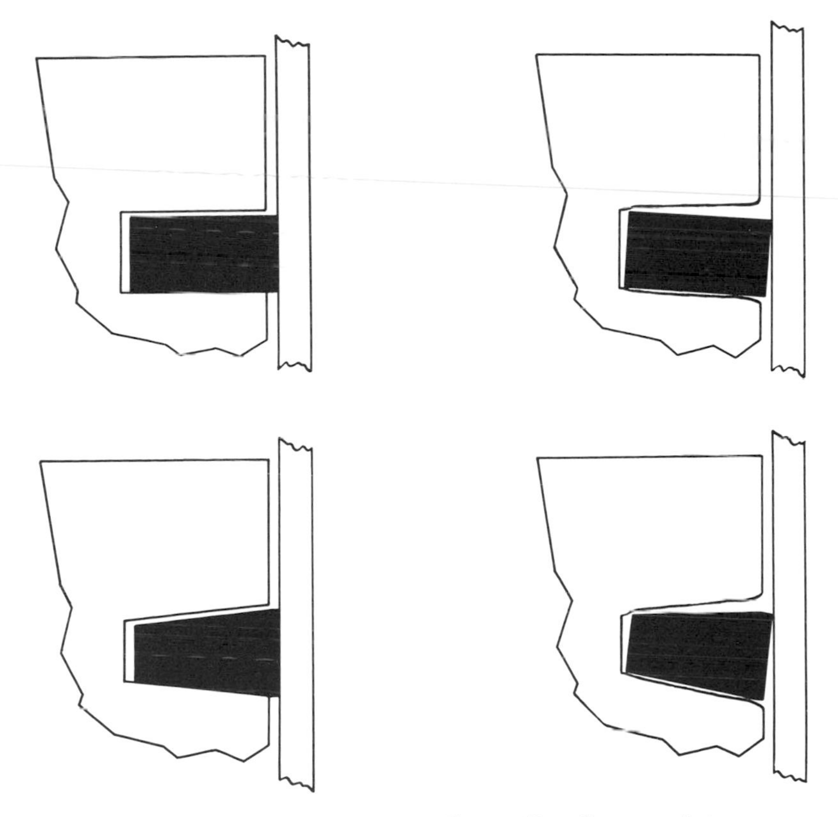

Courtesy Dana Corp., manufacturer of Perfect Circle Piston Rings

Fig. 18-27—New piston rings in a new piston or new grooves as shown on the left give good oil control. New rings in worn grooves as shown on the right give poor oil control.

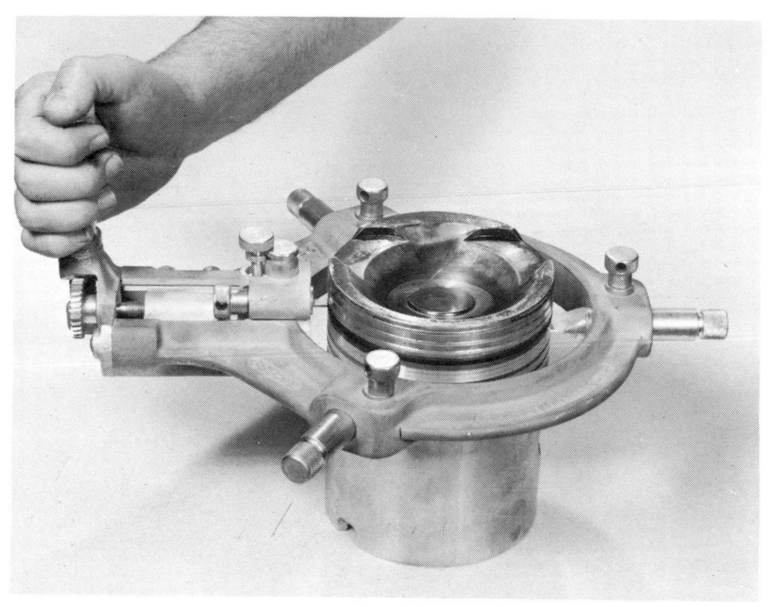

Courtesy Dana Corp., manufacturer
of Perfect Circle Piston Rings

Fig. 18-28—A device for remachining worn rectangular piston ring grooves to receive a standard width ring and a .024″ wide steel spacer or the next larger width ring and no spacer.

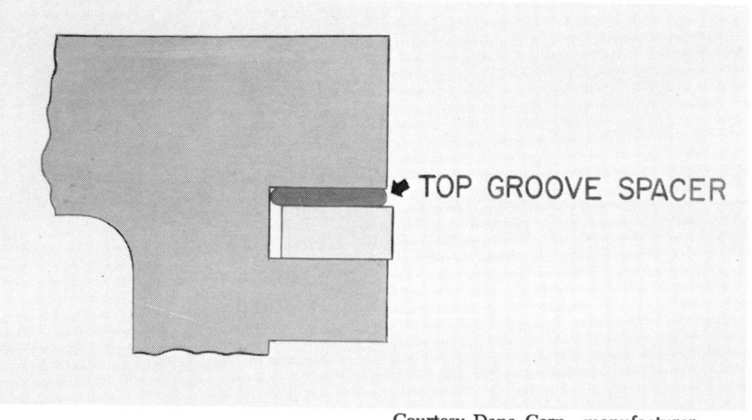

Courtesy Dana Corp., manufacturer
of Perfect Circle Piston Rings

Fig. 18-29—The heat-treated steel spacer is installed above the new ring in the remachined groove.

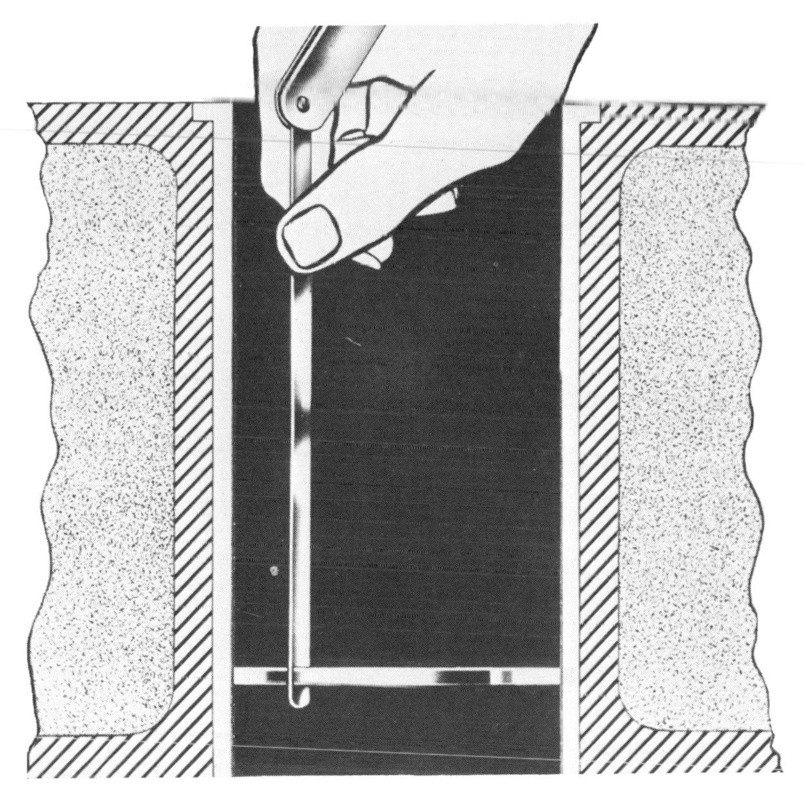

Courtesy Dana Corp., manufacturer of Perfect Circle Piston Rings

Fig. 18-30—Measuring end clearance.

pared to the scale on the Plastigage tube which gives a reading in thousandths of an inch and in millimeters.

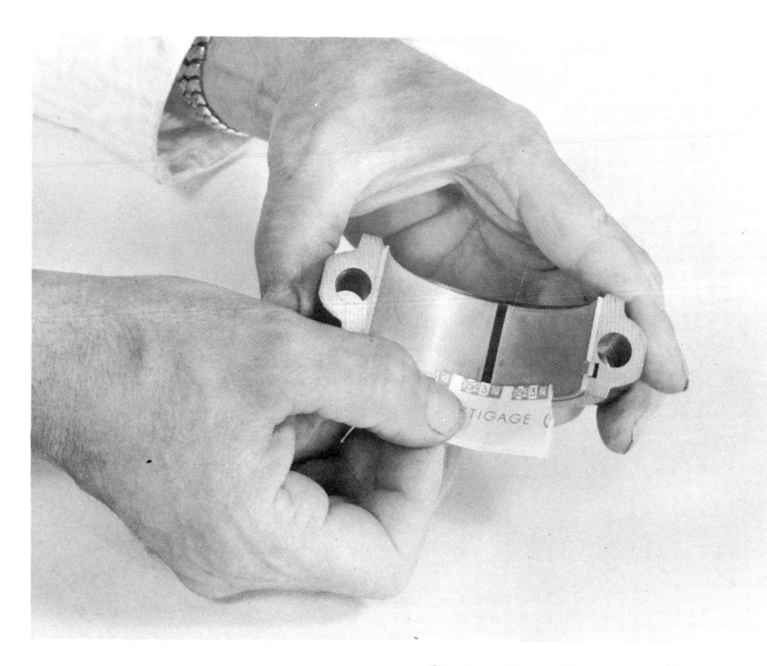

Courtesy Dana Corp., manufacturer
of Perfect Circle Piston Rings

Fig. 18-31—Checking bearing clearance with Plastigage. Lay a piece of Plastigage in the bearing and tighten the bearing to the recommended torque. Remove the bearing cap and compare the width of the flattened Plastigage to scale to determine bearing clearance.

QUESTIONS

1. What overhaul work on the tractor is usually considered to be minor in nature?
2. What overhaul work on the tractor is usually considered to be major repair work?
3. What can be learned about the condition of an engine by testing the compression in each cylinder?
4. In case of low compression, how can you determine whether the valves or rings are at fault?

5. Why is the correct valve clearance adjustment so important to valve life?
6. Why is the use of a torque wrench important when installing the head on an engine?
7. Why does the valve clearance change when the head bolts are tightened?
8. Why should the valves be adjusted with the engine not running on most late model tractors?
9. How can the crankshaft be turned on late model tractors?
10. How can you tell when a cylinder is at the TDC position on the compression stroke?
11. What is the firing order in a six cylinder engine?
12. What are the two possible firing orders in four cylinder engines with conventional crankshafts?

CHAPTER 19

TROUBLE-SHOOTING GUIDE

When trouble shooting, it will help to keep in mind that an engine has three basic needs—fuel-air mixture, compression and ignition. These basic needs must be satisfied whether the engine is gasoline, LP gas or diesel.

Failure to Start or Hard to Start

Fuel valve closed.
No fuel in the tank.
Improper type of fuel.
Water in the fuel supply.
Old fuel in the tank.
Clogged fuel strainer or filter.
No gasoline in the carburetor.
Fuel shut-off valve on the carburetor not working.
Liquid fuel in LP gas fuel lines.
Defective or wrong spark plugs.
No spark.
Distributor wires loose or installed wrong.
Pitted or burned ignition points.
Cracked or eroded distributor rotor.
Defective coil or condenser.
Poor timing of the distributor or diesel injection pump.
Dirty or faulty diesel injectors.
Defective cranking motor or battery.
Air in diesel fuel system.
Improper throttle position.
Faulty safety starting switch.
Flooded engine.

Clogged air cleaner.
Lack of compression.
Low air temperature when starting a diesel.
Lubricating oil too heavy.

Engine Runs Irregularly or Stalls Frequently

Engine incorrectly timed.
Poor or weak spark.
Dirty or faulty spark plugs.
Improper spark plug gap.
Defective coil or condenser.
Cracked distributor cap.
Defective ignition resistor or key switch.
Carburetor idle mixture not correct.
Carburetor load valve not set correctly.
Air in diesel fuel system.
Clogged fuel lines or filters.
Diesel injection nozzles dirty or stuck.
Faulty diesel injection pump.
Diesel injection pump out of time.
Intake manifold gaskets leaking.
Faulty or sticking engine valves.
Air intake restricted.
Low air temperature.
Low coolant temperature.
Insufficient valve clearance.
Governor sticking or out of adjustment.
Injection pump governor out of adjustment.
Low fuel pressure.

Engine Detonates or Pre-ignites

Wrong fuel.
Distributor timed too early.
Distributor advance mechanisms not working.
Carbon particles in the cylinder.

Faulty spark plugs.
Spark plugs with the heat range too high.

Engine Backfires

Carburetor mixture too lean.
Spark plug cables installed wrong.

Engine Knocks

Improper distributor or diesel injection pump timing.
Engine overheating.
Insufficient crankcase oil.
Low coolant temperature.
Worn or the wrong bearings or bushings.
Excessive crankshaft endplay.
Loose bearing caps.
Broken rings or loose pistons.
Loose piston pins.
Wrong grade of fuel.

Engine Overheats

Radiator fins bent or plugged with trash.
Low on coolant.
Low on crankcase oil.
Diluted crankcase oil.
Cooling system limed up and needs flushing.
Collapsed radiator hose.
Faulty radiator cap.
Defective thermostat.
Loose fan belt.
Use of low octane fuel or wrong type of fuel.
Improper ignition or injection pump timing.
Overloaded engine.
Distributor advance mechanism not working.
Temperature gauge defective.

Lack of Power

Engine overloaded.
Engine not up to correct temperature.
Overheated engine.
Crankcase oil too heavy.
Low on crankcase oil.
Governor sticking or out of adjustment.
Wrong type of fuel.
Restriction in fuel lines, strainers or filters.
Air in diesel fuel lines.
Fuel tank air vent obstructed.
Air intake restricted.
Dirty air cleaner.
Overheated intake air.
Dirty or faulty diesel injectors.
Diesel injection pump out of time.
Improper ignition timing.
Dirty or faulty spark plugs.
Ignition points burned or out of adjustment.
Cracked distributor cap.
Improper carburetor load adjustment.
Float level too low in carburetor.
Exhaust pipe clogged.
Poor compression.
Improper valve clearance.
Faulty engine valves.
Low engine speed.
Incorrect camshaft timing.
Improper hitching of implement.

Low Engine Oil Pressure

Engine low on oil.
Improper type of oil, oil too light.
Broken, loose or plugged oil lines.
Defective or dirty oil pressure regulating valve.

Oil pump strainer clogged.
Oil pump worn or not working correctly.
Worn bearings.

High Engine Oil Consumption

Crankcase oil too light.
Oil leaks.
Worn piston rings.
Worn bearings.
Crankcase breather pipe clogged.
Crankcase ventilator pump not working.
Worn valve guides or stem oil seals.
Oil pressure too high.
Engine speed too high.
Restricted air intake.
Restricted oil return passage from valve cover.

High Fuel Consumption

Engine overloaded.
Poor grade of fuel.
Improper valve clearance.
Clogged or dirty air cleaner.
Wrong viscosity oil.
Oil level low.
Poor compression due to worn piston rings or faulty valves.
Choke closed or partially closed on a gasoline engine.
Ignition out of time or injection pump out of time.
Improper carburetor adjustment.
Fuel leaks.
Engine not operating at proper temperature.
Diesel injection nozzles not operating properly.

Diesel Engine Emits Black or Gray Exhaust Smoke

Engine overloaded.
Improper fuel.

Excessive fuel rate.
Clogged or dirty air cleaner.
Dirty or faulty diesel injectors.
Low coolant temperature.
Injection pump out of time.
Turbocharger not functioning.

Diesel Engine Emits White Exhaust Smoke (indicates misfiring)

Cold engine.
Low coolant temperature.
Defective thermostat.
Improper type of fuel.
Faulty injectors.
Injection pump out of time.
Poor compression.

Gasoline Engine Emits Black Exhaust Smoke

Improper carburetor adjustment, too rich.
Clogged or dirty air cleaner.
Choke closed or partially closed.

Engine Emits Blue Exhaust Smoke (indicates high oil consumption)

Worn or stuck piston rings.
Low coolant temperature.
Restricted oil return passage from valve cover.

Spark Plug Fouling

Wrong heat range plug.
Low engine temperature.
Worn piston rings with excessive oil consumption.

Engine Stops

Fuel low in tank.
Restriction in fuel flow.
No fuel being delivered.
Air vent hole in fuel tank cap plugged.
Fuel shut-off valve closed or partially closed.
Dirty or clogged gasoline fuel strainer.
Diesel injection pump improperly timed to the engine.

Batteries Will Not Charge

Loose or corroded connections.
Sulfated or worn out batteries.
Loose fan belt.
Voltage regulator not functioning properly.

Starter Inoperative

Loose or corroded connections.
Low battery output.
Faulty starter.
Tractor in gear.

Starter Cranks Slowly

Loose or corroded connections.
Low battery output.
Crankcase oil too heavy.
Faulty starter.

Transmission Oil Overheats

Low oil supply.
Oil cooler air passages plugged.
Clogged transmission or hydraulic oil filter.
Excessive shifting under load.

CHAPTER 20

STORING THE TRACTOR FOR LONG PERIODS

Tractors that are to be unused for a month or more should be carefully prepared for storage in order to prevent damage. Some damage may not be apparent until after the tractor is put into use again.

Procedure

1. Warm the engine thoroughly, and drain the engine crankcase oil.
2. Replace the oil filter element, and fill the crankcase with new oil of the proper viscosity and API service rating. Run the engine about five minutes after refilling.
3. Drain, flush and fill the cooling system with clean soft water and with cooling system conditioner for summer storage, or with the recommended antifreeze solution for winter storage.
4. Add a specified amount of corrosion inhibitor to the transmission-hydraulic system (as recommended by one manufacturer).
5. Run the engine at a slow idle to circulate the coolant with the thermostat open and cycle all hydraulic functions to circulate the inhibitor to all parts of the hydraulic system.
6. Drain the fuel tank on all gasoline and diesel tractors. On gasoline tractors only, drain the fuel tank sediment bowl, and run the engine until it stops. Add corrosion inhibitor to the fuel tank of gasoline and diesel tractors.
7. Add the recommended amount of inhibitor to the crankcase of diesel or gasoline engines.

8. On gasoline or LP gas engines remove spark plugs and pour the recommended amount of inhibitor or one tablespoonful of SAE-30 lubricating oil through the spark plug hole into each cylinder. Crank the engine two or three times and replace the spark plugs.
9. On diesel engines loosen air intake pipe from the manifold, and place the recommended amount of inhibitor in the manifold. Reconnect the air intake pipe, and turn the engine over two revolutions slowly with the key switch off.

   One manufacturer recommends partially filling the fuel tank with a mixture of one-half pure white kerosene and one-half SAE 10-W oil, enough to run the engine 10 or 15 minutes, then running the engine at 1,000 to 1,200 RPM until the engine stops from lack of fuel.

   The same manufacturer recommends removing the nozzle bodies to spray about one ounce of SAE-30 oil into each cylinder, then to crank the engine two or three revolutions before reinstalling the nozzle bodies, after cleaning the gasket seats and installing new gaskets.
10. If corrosion inhibitor is not introduced into the valve area, the valve cover should be cleaned and removed and SAE-50 oil should be slushed over the valves, rocker arms and push rods. Coat the inside of the valve housing cover with the oil, and replace the valve cover. Do not run the engine.
11. Service the air cleaner.
12. Loosen the fan belt.
13. Remove, clean and store the batteries in a cool, dry place where the temperature will not get below freezing. Keep the electrolyte up to the correct level, charge the batteries before storing them and bring them up to a full charge every 30 days while in storage.
14. Seal all openings on the tractor with plastic bags and heavy tape. The openings to be sealed are: all air cleaner inlets, exhaust muffler, crankcase breather tube, fuel tank ventilated cap, radiator overflow hose and the transmission-hydraulic filler cap and breather. Sealing the openings keeps

condensation of moisture from the air to a minimum inside the engine during storage.

15. Coat exposed metal surfaces, such as axles and piston rods of hydraulic cylinders with corrosion preventative or with grease.
16. Block up the tractor so the tires are clear of the ground and protect them from sunlight and heat.
17. Block the clutch pedal in the disengaged position.
18. Clean the exterior of the tractor and touch up scratched or chipped painted surfaces.
19. Store the tractor in a dry protected place. If the tractor must be stored outside, cover it with waterproof canvas or other waterproof covering.

CHAPTER 21

PREPARING THE TRACTOR FOR SERVICE AFTER STORAGE

After the tractor has been idle for some time, whether or not it has been prepared for storage as suggested, it should be carefully serviced before being used.

Procedure

1. Remove seals from all openings on the tractor.
2. Check the air pressure in the tires and let the tractor down off the blocks.
3. Install fully charged battery or batteries, and connect battery cables correctly.
4. If the valve cover and valves were coated with SAE-50 oil, remove the valve cover, and flush the inside of the cover and the valves, rocker arms and push rods with a mixture of one-half kerosene and one-half SAE-10W oil. Then crank the engine a few revolutions to make sure all valves are working and none are sticking. Install a new gasket, and replace the valve cover.
5. Fill the fuel tank with fresh fuel.
6. Check the engine and transmission-hydraulic system oil levels, and add oil if necessary.
7. Check and, if necessary, fill the cooling system to the proper level.
8. Release the clutch pedal.
9. If oil was put into the cylinders through the spark plug holes, remove the plugs, and pour a mixture of one-half gasoline and one-half SAE-10W oil into each cylinder. About one ounce (two tablespoonfuls) per cylinder should be enough.

Crank the engine rapidly until excess oil is blown out of the spark plug holes. This operation is usually necessary to loosen any tight piston rings and wash old oil from the pistons and valves.

10. Install the spark plugs after cleaning and setting the gaps. Use new spark plug gaskets.
11. Check and clean the air cleaner if necessary.
12. Bleed the diesel fuel system of any air that might have accumulated.
13. Perform the 600 hour service jobs as it will help maintain the power and efficiency of the engine.
14. Start the engine and run it at a slow idle several minutes to make sure the tractor is in operating condition before putting it under a full load.

Part IV

SMALL ENGINES

CHAPTER 22

SMALL ENGINE MAINTENANCE

The maintenance of small engines of the type used on compact tractors, lawnmowers and garden tillers is similar to the maintenance of tractor engines with some exceptions.

Courtesy International Co.

Fig. 22-1—A compact riding tractor.

COOLING SYSTEM

Small engines are primarily air cooled, and the maintenance of the cooling system is critical, extremely important and often neglected on compact tractors. The cooling system consists of cooling fins, shrouds to direct the air and fins on the flywheel which serves as a fan to blow the air over the fins to dissipate the heat of the engine. Damage occurs when the cooling fins become clogged with grass and debris. The fins and fan screen must be cleaned as often as needed but should be checked at least every 25 hours.

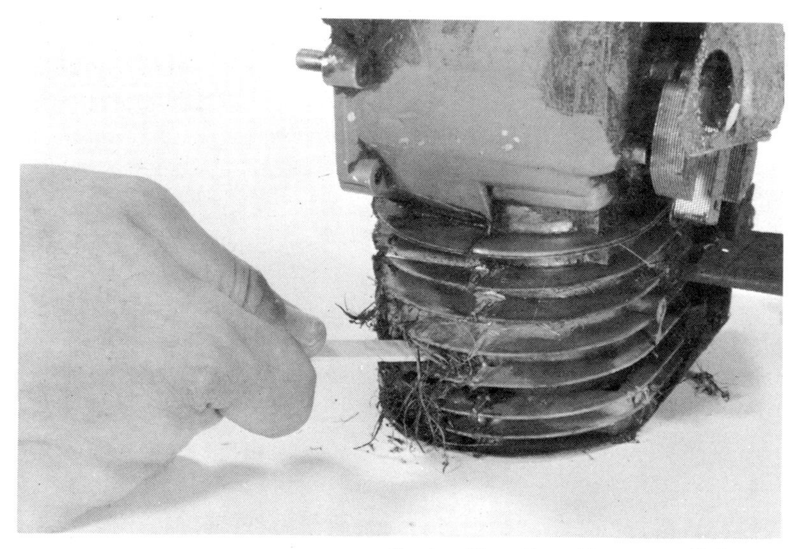

Courtesy Dana Corp., Hagerstown, Ind.

Fig. 22-2—Clean the cooling fins often. This engine overheated.

LUBRICATION

When breaking-in a new four-cycle engine, change the oil at the end of the first 2 to 5 hours of operation and then every 25 hours. Follow the manufacturer's recommendation closely for each engine. Service the air cleaner when the oil is changed. Drain the oil when the engine is warm. After the oil is well drained, fill with the correct quality and weight of oil recommended for the anticipated temperature conditions for the period the oil will be in the engine. The weight oil used in the summer when the temperature is above 40°F will not adequately lubricate the engine under winter conditions. If the engine is going to be used in the winter, a lighter weight oil must be used.

The engine manufacturer will usually recommend an SAE-30 weight oil when temperatures are above 40°F or SAE-10W-30 or SAE-10W-40 if SAE-30 is not available. When temperatures are below 40°F, the recommendation is usually SAE-5W-20 or SAE-5W-30. If these are not available, use SAE-10W or SAE-10W-30. If the temperature is below 0°F, the recommendation is to use SAE-10W or SAE-10W-30 diluted with 10% kerosene.

Check the Operator's Manual for the weight oil to use. Some manufacturers do not approve the use of multi-viscosity oils in their engines.

Keeping enough oil in the engine is as important as changing the oil at regular intervals. Check the engine oil level each day before starting it. Have the engine on a level surface when checking the oil. Fill the engine to overflowing or to the full mark on the dipstick. Check the oil level every 5 hours of continuous operation.

Some small four-cycle engines are lubricated by a dipper on the connecting rod bearing cap which dips into and splashes the oil up to the main bearings camshaft and cylinder. Other engines are lubricated by a gear-driven oil slinger and others by a gear- or cam-driven oil pump. When the oil level gets low, these devices cannot circulate enough oil, and the engine is damaged from lack of oil.

When it is necessary to add some oil to the engine, it usually indicates the need for an oil change. The recommended 25 hour oil change period is for average to good operating conditions. The oil should be changed every 12 hours under dusty conditions.

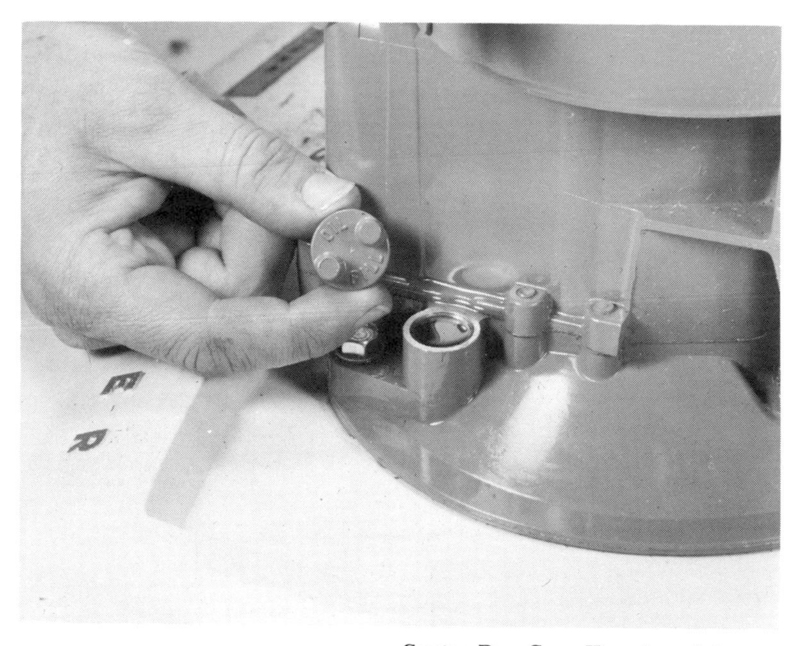

Courtesy Dana Corp., Hagerstown, Ind.

Fig. 22-3—Keep the oil level to the full mark.

Some engines have an extended oil fill and dipstick for convenience. Caution must be used to make sure the engine is not overfilled. Excessive oil will make the engine smoke and tends to shorten engine life by burning in the region of the upper piston rings, causing them to stick.

The quality of oil used is very important because of the high temperature and high speed conditions under which a small engine operates. Oil having an API classification of "MS," "SC" or "SD" should be used. These are high quality detergent oils which keep the engine clean and help retard the formation of gum and varnish deposits. The use of a non-detergent oil will void the warranty on some small engines. The only difference between short engine life and long engine life is the maintenance program followed by the operator.

A small engine maintained properly will last about 1,000 hours. An overhaul with new piston rings should make it last another 800 hours.

TROUBLE SHOOTING

When trouble shooting a small engine, first check the three things any engine must have to start and run:

Compression
Ignition (a hot spark at the plug)
Carburetion (fuel and air into the cylinder)

Check the compression by cranking the engine to the point of strongest resistance, and note whether the engine snaps back. If there seems to be no resistance, check to see if the spark plug is tight and its gasket is in place.

Check the ignition by removing the cable from the spark plug, and attach a spark tester, a special test plug with about a 3/16″ to 1/4″ gap, or hold the spark plug cable about 3/16″ away from some metal surface on the engine and crank the engine. If a good fat spark will jump a 3/16″ gap, the trouble is not in the ignition but may be in the spark plug. Check the spark plug and replace it with a new one if the tip is fouled or burned. Never have a spark plug from a small engine sandblasted. Some of the abrasive grit may remain in the plug and get into the engine and damage the rings and cylinder wall.

Check the carburetion by holding a thumb over the spark plug hole while cranking the engine a few turns. Your thumb should be moist with gas if fuel is reaching the cylinder. If there is no gas getting to the cylinder, check the vent in the gas tank cap, check for fuel in the tank, check to see that fuel is getting to the carburetor and check until you find the obstruction.

Engine Fails to Start or Starts with Difficulty

No fuel in the tank.
Shut-off valve closed.

Obstructed screen or fuel line.
Water in fuel.
Old fuel in tank.
Leaking carburetor mounting gaskets.
Engine not choked enough.
Remote controls to choke not adjusted correctly.
Engine over-choked.
Improper carburetor adjustment.
Fouled spark plug.
Faulty magneto coil or condenser.
Shorted ground wire.
Partially sheared flywheel key.
Air cleaner plugged.
Blown head gasket.
Loose rotary lawn mower cutter blade.
Worn cutter blade mounting hub.

Engine Knocks

Loose flywheel.
Loose cutter blade.
Loose cutter blade mounting hub.
Low on oil.
Loose or worn connecting rod.
Worn cylinder.
Improper magneto timing.

Engine Misses under Load

Spark plug fouled.
Improper spark plug gap.
Faulty magneto coil or condenser.
Pitted magneto breaker points.
Improper carburetor adjustment.
Improper valve clearance.
Weak valve spring.
Crankcase seals leaking.

Engine Lacks Power

Choke partially closed.
Improper carburetor adjustment.
Incorrect armature air gap.
Magneto improperly timed.
Pitted magneto breaker points.
Incorrect breaker point gap.
Low on crankcase oil.
Air cleaner dirty.
Valves leaking.
Blown head gasket.
Engine overheating.
Grass cuttings building up under cutter deck.
Worn piston or rings.
Crankcase seals leaking.
Exhaust ports plugged on 2-cycle engine.

Courtesy Dana Corp., Hagerstown, Ind.

Fig. 22-4—Clean the exhaust ports in a 2-cycle engine about every 25 hours of operation.

Engine Overheats

Engine improperly timed.
Carburetor load valve adjusted too lean.
Cooling fins obstructed or plugged.
Screen on flywheel obstructed.
Excessive load on engine.
Low on crankcase oil.
Excessive carbon in combustion chamber.
Pulleys too tight.

Engine Surges or Runs Unevenly

Fuel tank cap vent hole plugged.
Leak in carburetor mounting gaskets.
Governor parts sticking or binding.
Carburetor or governor linkage binding or sticking.

Engine Vibrates Excessively

Bent crankshaft.
Bent cutter blade or out of balance blade.
Worn cutter blade mounting hub.
Mounting bolts loose.
Mounting deck or plate cracked.

Crankcase Breather Passing Oil

Engine speed too fast.
Loose oil fill cap or damaged gasket.
Oil level too high.
Breather mechanism damaged or worn.
Breather mechanism dirty.
Drain hole in breather box clogged.
Breather mechanism installed wrong or gaskets missing.
Piston rings not seated properly.
Piston ring end gaps aligned.

High Oil Consumption

Worn rings or piston.
Excessive load on engine.
Engine speed too fast.
Oil level too high.
Loose or damaged oil fill cap.
Breather mechanism damaged or dirty.
Piston ring end gaps aligned.
Piston rings not seated properly.
Damaged or worn seals on end of crankshaft.

GENERAL REFERENCE LIST

Air Cooled Engine Mechanics Manual, Engine Service Association, 710 N. Plankinton, Milwaukee, WI 53203

Diesel Fuel Grades, American Society for Testing Materials, 1916 Race St., Philadelphia, PA 19103

Engine Service Classifications, API Bulletin 1509, American Petroleum Institute, 1801 K St., N.W., Washington, DC 20006

Farm Gas Engines and Tractors, Jones, McGraw-Hill Book Co., Inc., New York, NY 10020

Farm Power, Moses and Frost, John Wiley & Sons, Inc., New York, NY 10016

Fundamentals of Machine Operations, Deere & Company Service Publications, John Deere Rd., Moline, IL 61265:

"Tractors"
"Safety"
"Preventive Maintenance"

Fundamentals of Service Manuals, Deere & Company Service Publications, John Deere Rd., Moline, IL 61265:

"Bearings and Seals"
"Electrical Systems"
"Engines"
"Hydraulics"
"Power Trains"
"Shop Tools"

I and T Shop Service Master Manual Set, Intertec, 9221 Quivira Rd., Overland Park, KS 66212

Mechanics in Agriculture, Phipps, The Interstate Printers & Publishers, Inc., Danville, IL 61832

Repair Instructions, Briggs and Stratton Corp., Milwaukee, WI 53201

Small Engines, Vol. I and II, AAVIM, 120 Engineering Center, Athens, GA 30602

Small Engines Service Manual, Intertec, 9221 Quivira Rd., Overland Park, KS 66212

Small Gas Engines, Roth, Goodheart-Willcox Company, 123 W. Taft Dr., South Holland, IL 60473

INDEX

L

M

O

P

R

S

T

V

W